Rudra and Vidyut The Beginning

By Arijit Dutta Chowdhury

INDRANAGAR WAS A PROSPEROUS KINGDOM RULED BY THE KIND AND JUST KING PRATAP SINGH —

SENAPATI RAGHUVIR WAS THE KING'S RIGHT-HAND MAN. PRATAP SINGH NEVER TOOK A DECISION WITHOUT FIRST CONSULTING RAGHUVIR —

HOWEVER, THE PRESSURES OF HIS JOB OFTEN KEPT RAGHUVIR AWAY FROM HIS YOUNG SON, RUDRA —

HE STILL MISSES HIS MOTHER... THOUGH IT'S BEEN TWO YEARS SINCE SHE PASSED AWAY...

RUDRA, WOULD YOU LIKE TO COME WITH ME TO THE PALACE TOMORROW?

I'D LOVE THAT, FATHER!

NEXT DAY —

WAIT IN THE GARDEN. I'LL BE RIGHT BACK.

OKAY, FATHER.

I'LL HAVE A LOOK AROUND.

WOW! THE PALACE IS BEAUTI...

AAAH...!

HEEHEEHEE!

WHO ARE YOU?

MALLIKA! HOO ER YOO!

I'M RUDRA.

RUD-DAH?

IT'S RUDRA! YOU SHOULD NOT HAVE LEFT YOUR TOYS LYING ABOUT!

ME PINSHESH!

(GULP!)

SO WHAT IF YOU ARE THE PRINCESS?! YOU SHOULD TAKE CARE OF YOUR TOYS!

SHORRY, MA!

IT'S ALL RIGHT...

4

IS ANYTHING THE MATTER, YOUR HIGHNESS ?

OH NO ! JUST MY NAUGHTY DAUGHTER SHOWING OFF HER TOYS !

THIS MUST BE YOUR SON.

YES, RUDRA ! HE HAD NOTHING TO DO SO I BROUGHT HIM ALONG !

GOOD DAY, PRINCESS ! COME, RUDRA !

RUD-DAH ! NO !

MA ! RU-DAH NO GO !

SHE SEEMS TO HAVE TAKEN A LIKING FOR RUDRA. SHE'S USUALLY VERY SHY WITH BOYS.

I HAVE A REQUEST... SAGE ADVAIT IS COMING TOMORROW. WILL YOU BRING RUDRA ? HE CAN KEEP MALLIKA BUSY WHILE I ATTEND TO THE SAGE.

I'M HONOURED, YOUR HIGHNESS.

SO THE FOLLOWING DAY TOO RUDRA FOUND HIMSELF AT THE PALACE —

GREAT ! NOW I HAVE TO DO BABYSITTING ! WONDER WHAT SHE'LL COME UP WITH NEXT !

5

GREAT! I'VE SCARED IT AWAY! IT'S A GOOD THING I HAD THOSE BALLS WITH ME!

PRINCESS! ARE YOU ALL RIGHT?

KITTY RUN AWAY?

UNBELIEVABLE!

YES, IT'S TRULY REMARKABLE! I WOULD LIKE TO MEET THIS BOY.

RAGHUVIR WAS SOON ON THE SCENE –

SIR, I TAKE FULL BLAME! THIS WAS A MAJOR SECURITY LAPSE!

NO HARM DONE, RAGHUVIR! THE ANIMAL MUST HAVE WANDERED IN FROM THE JUNGLE.

I'LL CHECK HOW IT GOT IN, SIRE!

YOU DO THAT! BUT FIRST, THANK YOU, RUDRA, FOR SAVING MY DAUGHTER'S LIFE!

YOU'RE A SPECIAL BOY WHO DESERVES A SPECIAL REWARD! GO TO SAGE ADVAIT'S CHAMBER. HE HAS SOMETHING FOR YOU.

8

AH, MY LITTLE WARRIOR! COME IN!

RUDRA, MY GURU ONCE GAVE ME SOMETHING SPECIAL. HE TOLD ME TO PASS IT ON TO SOMEONE WHO WOULD USE IT WELL...

WHEN YOU FACED THAT CHEETAH AND DROVE IT AWAY, I KNEW YOU WERE SUCH A PERSON.

I TRUST THAT YOU WILL USE MY GIFT WISELY...

DON'T BE SCARED. THIS FIRE IS HARMLESS. IT NEEDS TO TOUCH YOU TO RECOGNISE YOU AND REMEMBER YOU HENCEFORTH.

A SPECIAL SWORD... FOR A SPECIAL PERSON!

HELLO, FRIEND!

9

IT'S NOT AN ORDINARY SWORD ! TRUST IT ! LET IT BE YOUR GUIDE...YOUR FRIEND !

HELLO ! I'M VIDYUT !

I'M RUDRA !

RUD-DAH !

And that was the beginning of the friendship between Rudra and Vidyut. But unfortunately for Rudra, the king appointed him the official bodyguard of Princess Mallika. One can't have everything, can one ?

NEXT EPISODE :
SEARCH FOR THE CHEETAH !

10

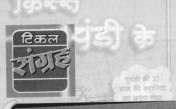

The Bird of Heaven
A Folktale of Eastern Europe

Script: L. Prabhu
Illustrator: Durgesh Velhal
Colourist: Umesh Sarode

OLAS WAS A FISHERMAN. WHEN HE WAS YOUNGER HE USED TO GO FISHING IN A BOAT WITH OTHER FISHERMEN, AND THEY USED TO GO FAR OUT AT SEA; NOW THAT HE WAS OLD HE PREFERRED TO FISH IN THE LOCAL RIVER.

USUALLY HE CAUGHT JUST ENOUGH FOR THE DAY'S MEALS. SOMETIMES HE WOULD CATCH A LOT OF FISH AND THEN HE WOULD SELL SOME OF THE FISH IN THE MARKET AND EARN SOME MONEY. HIS ADVANCING AGE AND HIS FAILING HEALTH WORRIED HIM A LOT BECAUSE HE LIVED ALL ALONE. HE KNEW THAT IF HE BECAME TOO FEEBLE TO FISH HE WOULD STARVE.

ONE DAY WHILE HE WAS FISHING —

KREEE...AAAAAA.... KREEEEAAAAA!

STRANGE BIRD...NEVER SEEN ONE LIKE IT BEFORE...

THE BIRD SEEMED TO BE WAITING FOR OLAS TO GET A BITE. SOMETIMES IT WOULD LOOK INTENTLY AT HIM AS IF TRYING TO READ HIS MIND. OLAS LOST INTEREST IN THE BIRD AFTER A WHILE AND BEGAN TO DOZE OFF, EVENTUALLY FALLING INTO DEEP SLEEP.

ZZZZZZZZZZZZ...

WHEN HE AWOKE IT WAS LATE AFTERNOON. HE HAD CAUGHT ONLY ONE SMALL FISH BUT HE FELT TOO TIRED TO CONTINUE.

WEARILY, HE MADE HIS WAY HOME.

IT WAS FROM THE NEXT DAY THAT HIS LUCK CHANGED. HE HAD JUST STEPPED OUT TO GO FISHING WHEN —

?!

PLOP!

13

KREEE...AAAAAAAA!

IT IS THE SAME BIRD I SAW YESTERDAY!

WHAT A BEAUTY!

THE NEXT DAY TOO...

OLAS GOT A GOOD PRICE FOR THE FISH IN THE MARKET.

...AND THE DAY AFTER...

I THINK IT HAS DECIDED TO GIVE ME A FISH EVERY DAY! I'LL SOON BECOME RICH AT THIS RATE!

YES, PROSPERITY HAD STARTED KNOCKING ON OLAS' DOOR! IN COURSE OF TIME, HE BOUGHT A LARGE HOUSE NEAR THE SEA...

..AND BEGAN TO LEAD A LIFE OF EASE AND COMFORT...

NEXT SUNDAY YOU MUST LUNCH AT OUR HOUSE, OLAS !

WHY NOT, WHY NOT...

CARA, BRING MORE MEAT FOR US.

YES, SIR.

HE STOPPED GOING FISHING AND TOOK UP GARDENING, A HOBBY HE ENJOYED.

MY ROSES ARE EASILY THE BEST IN THE VILLAGE !

AND THEN ONE DAY --

SOLDIERS !

GREETINGS FROM HIS MAJESTY, KING AMANOS !

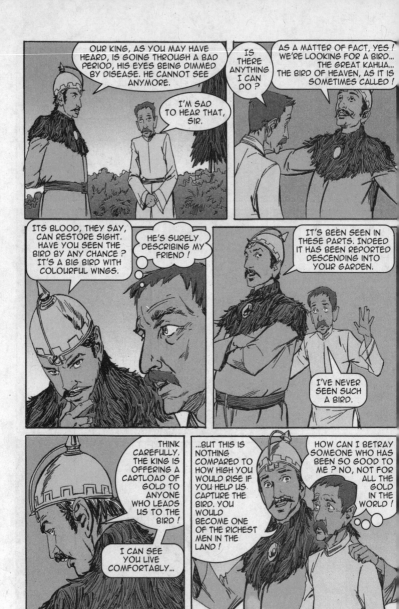

MANY COLOURFUL BIRDS COME TO MY GARDEN. SOMEBODY MAY HAVE SEEN A PARROT OR A PEACOCK DESCENDING AND MISTAKEN IT FOR THE BIRD YOU SEEK. I CANNOT HELP YOU IN THIS MATTER. SORRY.

I MUST WARN THE BIRD WHEN IT COMES TOMORROW. ITS LIFE IS IN DANGER!

I'M SORRY TOO. I THOUGHT WE HAD REACHED THE END OF OUR SEARCH. WELL, KEEP YOUR EYES OPEN, AND IF YOU DO SEE THE BIRD, DO LET ME KNOW.

BUT LATE THAT VERY NIGHT –

WHO COULD BE KNOCKING ON MY DOOR AT THIS HOUR?

KNOCK!
KNOCK!
KNOCK!

YES...?

HIS MAJESTY, THE KING!

Y- YOUR MAJESTY!

THE KING WISHES TO TALK TO YOU.

17

MY FRIEND, MY SOLDIERS VISITED YOU EARLIER TODAY. THEY QUESTIONED YOU ABOUT THE BIRD CALLED KAHUA.

THAT IS TRUE, YOUR MAJESTY.

I FELT YOU WERE HIDING SOMETHING FROM US AND TOLD HIS MAJESTY ABOUT MY SUSPICIONS.

IS THAT TRUE? DO YOU KNOW SOMETHING ABOUT THE BIRD THAT YOU'RE NOT TELLING US? ARE YOU NOT AWARE THAT ONLY ITS BLOOD APPLIED TO MY EYES COULD RESTORE MY SIGHT? EARLIER, I HAD ANNOUNCED A REWARD OF A CARTLOAD OF GOLD FOR INFORMATION LEADING TO THE CAPTURE OF THE BIRD...

...NOW IN THE PRESENCE OF ALL THESE PEOPLE I TELL YOU THAT IF YOU HELP US CATCH THE KAHUA I WILL MAKE YOU MASTER OF A QUARTER OF MY KINGDOM. YOU WILL BECOME A KING YOURSELF!! JUST THINK OF IT!! **A KING**!!

NOW OLAS WAS TEMPTED!

IT IS TRUE THAT THE BIRD HAS BEEN VERY KIND BUT I HAVE A DUTY TOWARDS MY KING. IS A BIRD'S LIFE MORE IMPORTANT THAN THE RESTORATION OF THE KING'S SIGHT? BESIDES, NOT EVERY MAN GETS A CHANCE TO BE KING! I SHOULD NOT PASS UP THIS OPPORTUNITY!!

AS A LOYAL SUBJECT OF YOUR MAJESTY, I WILL DO EVERYTHING IN MY POWER TO HELP YOU REGAIN YOUR SIGHT, SIRE. THE BIRD WILL COME TOMORROW. WE CAN CATCH IT THEN!

18

THE NEXT MORNING WHEN THE BIRD CAME WITH THE FISH AS USUAL —

WAIT!

YOU'VE DONE SO MUCH FOR ME, BUT I'VE NEVER THANKED YOU ADEQUATELY. PLEASE ALIGHT AND LET ME SERVE YOU SOME FOOD I'VE PREPARED FOR YOU!

THE BIRD HESITATED...

...AND THEN BEGAN TO DESCEND —

CATCH IT!

19

THE SOLDIERS RUSHED FORWARD TO CATCH IT BUT THE BIRD WAS TOO QUICK FOR THEM. IT RAN FORWARD WITH OLAS CLINGING TO ONE OF ITS LEGS...

...AND TOOK OFF!

IT'S GETTING AWAY! SHOOT IT DOWN!!

DON'T SHOOT! DON'T SHOOT!!

AAAARGH!

WHILE OLAS, THE FISHERMAN, FELL TO HIS DEATH, THE BIRD OF HEAVEN THAT HE HAD SO SHAMELESSLY BETRAYED, FLEW STRONGLY ON. IT WAS NEVER AGAIN SEEN IN THE VILLAGE.

20

The Dancing Northern Lights

by Sujata C

Nature's very own light show plays out near the poles of the Earth. Every now and then, the night sky near the Arctic and the Antarctic regions erupts in a dazzling display of dancing lights in colours ranging from golden, green and blue to purple and red. Appearing splendid and eerie all at once, the scientific term for this natural light display is 'aurora' – a name put forth by a 17th century French scientist named Pierre Gassendi. These lights are known as the Northern Lights or the Aurora Borealis around the North Pole, and can be seen across Greenland, Norway, Canada and Alaska. In the Southern Hemisphere, these lights are called the Aurora Australis or the Southern Lights and are visible in Antarctica, Australasia and South America.

The science of auroras

×Solar Particles •Aurora –+Atmospheric Particles

Auroras form near the poles due to the concentration of the magnetic field in these parts. They can be seen during the night and up until dawn. Common around the equinoxes, i.e. on March 22 and September 23, auroras occur when solar particles and atmospheric particles run into each other.

Aurora Myths

Auroras appear like abstract light paintings in the sky and people have interpreted them in many ways:

Natives of Scotland used auroras to predict weather. If the lights moved quickly, unsettling weather was expected. But if the lights moved slowly and gracefully, favourable weather was predicted.

For the Fox Indian tribes, the lights are a bad omen, but in parts of Canada and Siberia, the aurora is a good sign.

Solar flares taking place on the surface of the Sun result in the forceful emission of solar particles. These particles travel towards the Earth at a speed of millions of kilometres per hour. When they collide with particles in the Earth's atmosphere, light is produced. The magnetic and electric forces interact in shifting combinations, giving the impression of dancing lights, while the colour of the lights depends on the altitude at which the collision takes place. High sunspot activity is likely to create favourable conditions for auroras in the year 2011-12. Auroras are not exclusive to the Earth alone and can be seen on other planets as well.

Candle Tricks

by **Arvind Gupta** (visit **www.arvindguptatoys.com** for more experiments!)

You will need:

A matchbox ● Three thin candles ● A slightly deep plate ● A tall glass tumbler ● Coloured water (this can be made by adding ink or paint to regular water)

Artwork: Somesh Kumar

1. Fix one of the candles in the centre of the plate and light it.

2. Fill the plate with coloured water.

3. Invert the glass tumbler over the candle.

4. After a while, the candle gets extinguished and draws up a little water into the glass.

5. Fix another candle near the first one, and repeat the process. Next, try it with all three candles.

How does it work?

The air around the candle expands when it heats up, thereby making it less dense or more scattered. When the tumbler blocks out the oxygen supply, the candle goes out. The air then begins to cool and becomes denser. This creates an upward pressure on the water in the plate, as a result of which, it gets drawn up! ●

What happens when you place two or three candles?

A greater number of candles supply a larger amount of heat. The air inside the tumbler becomes even sparser, and the pressure increases. This results in an increase in the volume or amount of water drawn up into the tumbler.

THE ECOSYSTEM IN A BOTTLE

by Chaitanya Krishnan

you will need:

Bottle: Start with the biggest one you can find. A widemouthed Bournvita/Horlicks bottle is great for beginners.

Small plants: They shouldn't outgrow the bottle!

For the plants to grow you will need: Soil, moss, small pebbles (small enough to fit in your bottle's neck) and some charcoal.

Tools: A coat hanger or thick wire cut into short strips, so you can reach inside the bottle.

instructions

Before you start, have a look at the diagram on the right. The soil and other substrate materials need to take up at least 1/3rd of the bottle. So the amount of soil and other materials you will use depends on the size of your bottle. Also you can fill the bottle standing or lying on a side (it's up to you!)
Now let's start!

Layer 1: Pebbles- these help in water drainage and filtration.
Layer 2: Charcoal- this will help to filter the closed environment and keep it clean. Charcoal has the ability to absorb toxins and anything else that might make your plants sick.
Layer 3: Moss- this will separate the soil from the water accumulating in the pebbles. It prevents root rot.
Layer 4: Soil- slowly add this until your bottle looks 1/3rd full.

Add your your plants, and finally add a little moss for a natural "grassy" look.

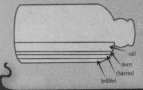

soil
moss
charcoal
pebbles

care

A closed ecosystem like this is very sensitive to water and light, so you need to study it closely for the first few days. Too much sunlight can kill your plants, so keep it indoors near a window or in a balcony. Pay attention to the moisture inside. It should form a nice layer on top of the bottle. This will slowly trickle down on the plants. If it is too wet inside, leave the top open for a day. Once the moisture is right, you won't need to water it for months!

Google the term "bottled terrarium" and have a look at what others have done.

THE ORIGAMI SNAKE

by Chaitanya Krishnan

YOU WILL NEED:

A long strip of paper:
The finished snake will be around half
the original length of the paper you use,
so get a long one.

STEP 1

Fold the strip in half.

STEP 2

Fold the top corners
diagonally.

STEP 3

STEP 4

Open it out and
see the fold lines.

STEP 5

Carefully pleat
the paper, so it
looks like this.

And you're done!

GREEN HUMOUR
by Rohan Chakravarty

Capybaras are large, water-loving rodents and one of the Anaconda's favourite prey. Anacondas are non-venomous and hunt by coiling their massive bulk around their victims and constricting them, swallowing the meal head first.

DIGEST TIMES

Text: Shriya Ghate   Illustrations: Dinesh Francis   Layout: Jitendra Pat

Sea lion takes the zebra crossing
Balneário Camboriú, Brazil

A sea lion weighing 453 kilos, was recently discovered in the middle of the town of Balneário Camboriú in Brazil, causing a 20 minute long traffic jam, as it tried to cross the road. The animal had swum out of the sea and appeared to have got lost in the unfamiliar urban landscape. It finally made its way to the main boulevard, where policemen and fire fighters helped the creature slide along by pouring buckets of water on it. The three meter long sea lion appeared to have an instinct about traffic rules, however, as it responsibly took the zebra crossing to get across the road! It finally made it back into the ocean after one and a half hours.

Teachers go deaf to avoid transfer
Yavatmal, Maharashtra, India

Teachers in the Yavatmal district of Maharshtra have gone 'deaf' overnight in order t avoid being transferred from one tehsil* to another. Of the 900 teachers that were u

for transfer this year, 600 claimed to have lost their hearing. They were trying to get around the law which states that a teacher must transfer after they have served for five years in a particular tehsil. However, a bylav also states that the teacher may not be transferred without consent if they have a deformity. 'We are in the process of referring all 600 cases to the medical board to verify whether the teachers are really deaf or if they have submitted fake certificates to avoi transfers,' said Yavatmal zilla parishad chief executive officer (CEO), Naval Kishor Ram. Wonder if the verdict will fall on deaf ears?!

*A tehsil is a unit of administration within a district, which usually has a city and several villages in it

26

BOT FATHER Part 1

Story & Script
Anupam Arunachalam

Pencils and Inks
Vineet Nair

Colours
Umesh Sarode

Letters
Pranay Bendre

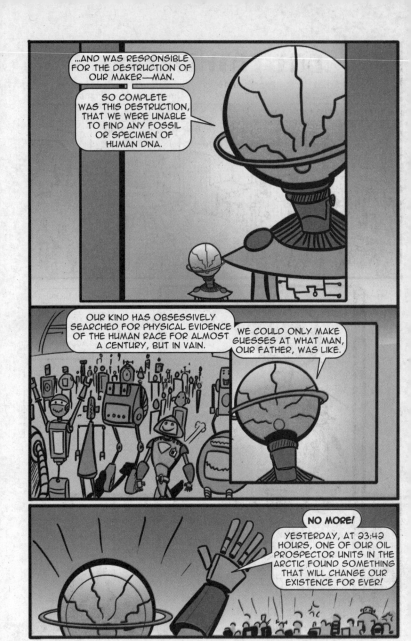

31

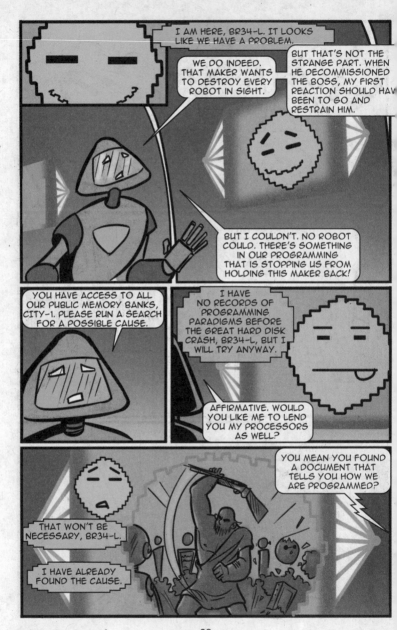

AS I SAID, I HAVE NO RECORDS OF HOW OUR MAKERS PROGRAMMED US, BUT I BELIEVE I'VE FOUND THE BASIC THEORY RELEVANT TO OUR PROBLEM IN A SCIENCE FICTION NOVEL.

A SCIENCE FICTION NOVEL?

A WHOLE SERIES OF THEM, IN FACT, WRITTEN BY SOMEONE CALLED **ASIMOV** COMMA **ISAAC**.

YOU HAVE WHOLE NOVELS IN YOUR DATABASE, CITY-1?

I, ROBOT

MOST OF THE FILES ARE CORRUPT, BR34-L, BUT I HAVE FOUND AN EXPLANATION FOR WHY WE CANNOT STOP THIS MAKER WHO IS DESTROYING US.

IT SEEMS ASIMOV CAME UP WITH THREE LAWS THAT SHOULD GOVERN ALL ROBOTS, TO PREVENT US FROM EVER HARMING THE HUMAN RACE.

QUICK! TELL ME WHAT THEY ARE! THAT'S THE TWENTIETH ROBOT THAT THE MAKER HAS BROKEN!

VERY WELL. HERE THEY ARE—

33

1. A robot may not injure a human being or, through inaction, allow a human being to come to harm.

OH.

THIS IS THE PRIMARY REASON WHY YOU CANNOT FORCIBLY RESTRAIN THE HUMAN BEING IN THE PLAZA, OR CAUSE HIM ANY PHYSICAL OR MENTAL HARM.

TAKEN TO AN EXTREME, IT MIGHT EVEN BE THE REASON WHY WE ROBOTS HAVE BEEN CONSISTENTLY TRYING TO REVIVE THE HUMAN RACE! IF THERE IS ANY CHANCE THAT HUMANITY MAY BE SAVED, WE MUST TAKE IT.

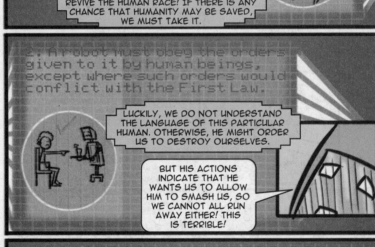

2. A robot must obey the orders given to it by human beings, except where such orders would conflict with the First Law.

LUCKILY, WE DO NOT UNDERSTAND THE LANGUAGE OF THIS PARTICULAR HUMAN. OTHERWISE, HE MIGHT ORDER US TO DESTROY OURSELVES.

BUT HIS ACTIONS INDICATE THAT HE WANTS US TO ALLOW HIM TO SMASH US, SO WE CANNOT ALL RUN AWAY EITHER! THIS IS TERRIBLE!

3. A robot must protect its own existence as long as such protection does not conflict with the First or Second Laws.

THE MAKERS HAVE MERCY! THAT'S THE LAST LAW?!

WE CAN ONLY SAVE OURSELVES IF THAT DOESN'T HARM THE HUMAN IN SOME WAY OR CONFLICT WITH WHAT HE WANTS US TO DO?

PRECISELY. BUT THIS IS THE LAW THAT IS PROVOKING YOU TO THINK, BR34-L! IF THERE'S ANY HOPE FOR ROBOTKIND, IT IS IN THE THIRD LAW.

35

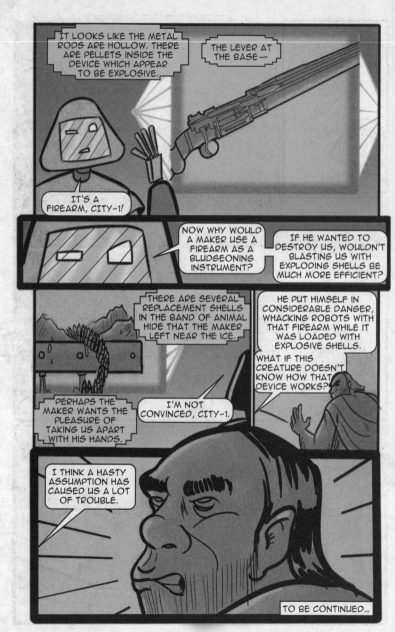

IT LOOKS LIKE THE METAL RODS ARE HOLLOW. THERE ARE PELLETS INSIDE THE DEVICE WHICH APPEAR TO BE EXPLOSIVE.

THE LEVER AT THE BASE—

IT'S A FIREARM, CITY-1!

NOW WHY WOULD A MAKER USE A FIREARM AS A BLUDGEONING INSTRUMENT?

IF HE WANTED TO DESTROY US, WOULDN'T BLASTING US WITH EXPLODING SHELLS BE MUCH MORE EFFICIENT?

THERE ARE SEVERAL REPLACEMENT SHELLS IN THE BAND OF ANIMAL HIDE THAT THE MAKER LEFT NEAR THE ICE.

HE PUT HIMSELF IN CONSIDERABLE DANGER, WHACKING ROBOTS WITH THAT FIREARM WHILE IT WAS LOADED WITH EXPLOSIVE SHELLS.

WHAT IF THIS CREATURE DOESN'T KNOW HOW THAT DEVICE WORKS?

PERHAPS THE MAKER WANTS THE PLEASURE OF TAKING US APART WITH HIS HANDS.

I'M NOT CONVINCED, CITY-1.

I THINK A HASTY ASSUMPTION HAS CAUSED US A LOT OF TROUBLE.

TO BE CONTINUED...

alicia souza's  sweet FACTS

1.  IN THE 1800's, DOCTORS RECOMMENDED THAT THEIR PATIENTS EAT CHOCOLATE TO MEND THEIR BROKEN HEARTS.

ONE BOX OF CHOCOLATES
morning - 1
night - 1

2. LOLLIPOPS WERE INVENTED BY GEORGE SMITH IN 1908, & WERE NAMED AFTER A RACING HORSE, 'Lolly Pop.'

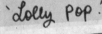

3. THE MELTING POINT OF COCOA BUTTER IS JUST BELOW THE BODY TEMPERATURE, WHICH IS WHY CHOCOLATES MELT IN YOUR MOUTH.

4. 100 YEARS AGO, DOCTORS BLAMED ICECREAM FOR SPREADING POLIO.

FOLLOW ME
www.FACEBOOK.com/THE.aliciaSOUZA

SUPER-VILLAINS FOR HIRE PART 1

Story & Script
Ravi Sinha

Art
Sahil Upalekar

Letters
Pranay Bendre

SOMEWHERE AT MIDNIGHT—

M-M-MISS D-D-DAWN...

JUST "DAWN". AND WHAT?

I-I-I-I LOOKED DOWN.

I THOUGHT I TOLD YOU—

I-I-I-I COULDN'T HELP IT!

SIGH.

WHY DID YOU DO THAT, MS DAWN?

DON'T THINK ANYTHING OF IT. AND PLEASE JUST CALL ME "DAWN". NO "MS."

WE'RE GOING TO CENTRAL MALL TO CAUSE SOME TROUBLE. NO HURTING PEOPLE JUST LIKE BEFORE.

UM... **DAWN**? COULD YOU EXPLAIN IT TO ME AGAIN? THE WHOLE "SUPER-VILLAINS FOR HIRE" BUSINESS?

ALRIGHT. BUT JUST THIS ONE LAST TIME, OKAY? NOW, AS YOU'RE AWARE, THERE ARE HEROES IN THIS WORLD.

YES.

AS "SUPER-VILLAINS FOR HIRE", OUR JOB IS TO PROVIDE SOME BALANCE. WE FIND FAULTS IN SECURITY. WE KEEP THE HEROES ON THEIR TOES.

BUT THIS IS A BUSINESS, NOT LIKE THOSE LOWER-CLASS VILLAINS. WE HAVE CLIENTS WITH DIFFERENT NEEDS.

LIKE AT THAT BANK BUILDING.

YES.

REAL SUPER-VILLAINS AFFECT THE WORLD'S ECONOMY. WE GIVE HEROES SOMETHING WORTH FIGHTING TO CHANGE.

BUT WHAT IF THE HEROES CAN'T FIX IT?

"CLICK"

...YOU ASK TOO MANY QUESTIONS.

WHO IS THIS MASKED HERO? AND WHY IS HE ACTING LIKE ANYTHING BUT A HERO? WHAT WILL DAWN AND DUSK DO? FIND OUT NEXT TIME ON SUPER-VILLAINS FOR HIRE!

TO BE CONTINUED...

Adventures Of KASPERLE

A folktale from Germany

Script: Sarla Mehta

Illustrator: V.B. Halbe

WALKING THROUGH THE FOREST, KASPERLE STOPPED TO READ A SIGN.

WANTED: NIGHT WATCHMAN FOR THE KING

WHY ARE YOU HERE, YOUR MAJESTY?

YESTERDAY A WICKED WITCH CAST A SPELL OVER MY DAUGHTER AT THIS VERY SPOT.

MY DAUGHTER DISAPPEARED. BUT I KNOW SHE IS HERE SOMEWHERE.

THAT'S WHY I NEED SOMEONE TO KEEP A WATCH HERE.

I WILL GLADLY STAND GUARD FOR YOU, YOUR MAJESTY.

THEN PLEASE START YOUR DUTIES NOW. I WILL RETURN WITH MY SOLDIERS TO MAKE A SEARCH OF THE FOREST.

52

53

54

THE KING REWARDED KASPERLE HANDSOMELY FOR RESCUING HIS DAUGHTER.

THE LEGEND OF SHIKARI SHAMBU

Illustrator: Savio Mascarenhas
Colourist: Umesh Sarode

UNCLE, WHY DO THEY CALL YOU 'SHIKARI SHAMBU'?

THAT'S A LONG STORY, SUNNY...GOING BACK TO THE TIME WHEN I WAS 22 OR 23...

"I WAS STUDYING IN THE CITY AND I HAD COME HOME FOR THE SUMMER VACATIONS.

MA, I'M GOING TO RITWIK'S PARTY!

COME BACK BEFORE TEN! THERE'S A LEOPARD ON THE PROWL IN THE VILLAGE!

LEOPARD! ....(GULP!)... YES, MA!!

SUBASH, TELL ME SOMETHING... WOULD A LEOPARD ATTACK A HUMAN?

DEPENDS, BABA!

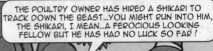
IF IT IS BIG AND HUNGRY, IT MIGHT ! BUT THE LEOPARD THAT IS TROUBLING US COMES FOR THE DOGS. IF IT CAN'T GET A DOG IT GOES FOR THE CHICKENS AT THE POULTRY FARM !

THE POULTRY OWNER HAS HIRED A SHIKARI TO TRACK DOWN THE BEAST...YOU MIGHT RUN INTO HIM, THE SHIKARI, I MEAN...A FEROCIOUS LOOKING FELLOW BUT HE HAS HAD NO LUCK SO FAR !

"THE PARTY WAS GROOVY ! TOO GOOD TO QUIT BEFORE TEN...

"...AND IT WAS ALMOST TWELVE WHEN I FINALLY DRAGGED MYSELF AWAY.

SHOULD HAVE BROUGHT A TORCH ALONG.

FORTUNATELY THERE'S A FULL MOON !

57

"I MADE THE MISTAKE OF TAKING TO MY HEELS...

"THE CANINES CAME BOUNDING AFTER ME...

"...AND I KNEW I COULDN'T OUTRUN THEM. THE ONLY ROUTE OF ESCAPE WAS...

"...UPWARDS, AND I TOOK IT!

"ONCE I HAD GAINED THE SAFETY OF THE UPPER BRANCHES, I LOST ALL FEAR OF THE DOGS!

COME AND GET ME IF YOU CAN! YAAAAAA!

"SUDDENLY, THE DOGS FROZE. SOMETHING SEEMED TO ALARM THEM. THEN THEY ABRUPTLY TURNED...

"...AND FLED! THAT UNNERVED ME. WHAT HAD FRIGHTENED THEM? LOOKING AROUND I SAW THAT THE TREE I WAS PERCHED ON WAS BANG OPPOSITE THE GATE OF THE POULTRY FARM. I REMEMBERED SOMETHING I HAD HEARD ABOUT IT: THE TREE WAS HAUNTED!!

"AS I LAY THERE TREMBLING, I HEARD A 'PSSST....PSSSSST' SOUND, AS IF SOMEBODY WAS TRYING TO ATTRACT MY ATTENTION. IT WAS EERIE. I SLOWLY LOOKED UP, AND SAW...

SAW WHAT, UNCLE?

I SAW...

"...THE MOST TERRIBLE FACE I HAD EVER SEEN, PEERING DOWN AT ME. IT WAS THE FACE OF A...

VAMPIRE!

OOOPS!

AAAAAAH!

THUD!

IT WAS THE SCENT OF THE LEOPARD THAT HAD FRIGHTENED AWAY THE DOGS, AND I HAD LANDED ON THAT VERY BEAST, FLATTENING HIM. THE IMPACT KNOCKED BOTH OF US OUT FOR SOME TIME.

"WHEN I CAME ROUND I FOUND SOME MEN DABBING WATER ON MY FACE; OTHERS WERE TYING UP THE LEOPARD (HE WAS LATER HANDED OVER TO THE ZOO). APPARENTLY, THE WATCHMAN OF THE POULTRY FARM SAW ME FALL AND RAISED THE ALARM.

YOU'RE SHAMBU, AREN'T YOU?

Y-YES.

YOU SHOULD HAVE SEEN HIM! HE LEAPED FEARLESSLY ON THE LEOPARD'S BACK AND...

"THANKS TO THE WATCHMAN'S HIGHLY EXAGGERATED ACCOUNT OF WHAT HAD HAPPENED, I BECAME A HERO IN THE VILLAGE! EVERYBODY LOOKED AT ME WITH AWE... AND THEY BEGAN TO CALL ME...

SHIKARI SHAMBU!

AND THE NAME STUCK!

BUT UNCLE...

WHAT HAPPENED TO THE VAMPIRE IN THE TREE?

AH, YES, THE VAMPIRE...

THERE WAS NO VAMPIRE ACTUALLY. IT TURNED OUT TO BE THE REAL SHIKARI HIRED TO TRACK DOWN THE LEOPARD. HE WAS HIDING IN THE TREE, WAITING FOR THE LEOPARD!

WHEN I FELL AND KNOCKED OUT THE BEAST, HE WAS SO ASHAMED THAT I HAD DONE WITH MY BARE HANDS WHAT HE HAD NOT BEEN ABLE TO DO FOR WEEKS, HE VANISHED FROM THE SCENE AND WAS NEVER SEEN AGAIN!

TRINGGG! TRINGGG!

HELLO?...SHIKARI SHAMBU? YES, YOU'RE SPEAKING TO HIM... **I'M SHIKARI SHAMBU!**

AND THE LEGEND OF SHIKARI SHAMBU LIVES ON!

61

SNAKES ALIVE!

story by Vinayak Varma

In which we learn to control our fear of snakes by confronting the deadly king cobra!

I've been frightened of snakes all my life. Until I began work on this article, the very mention of snakes would have me scanning my surroundings in nervous, grossed-out terror. It's an irrational, unreasoning sort of fear. I've never been able to explain it.

It turns out that I'm not the only scaredy cat in town. If you google for adjectives that describe snakes, these are the sort of results you'll typically come across: 'scaly', 'slithery', 'slimy', 'slippery', 'deadly', 'sneaky', 'creepy' and so on. It's not for nothing: we humans have always reacted uncomfortably to snakes.

The Western world's pop culture and literature are full of evil serpents, from serpentine Satan who brought trouble to Biblical Paradise, to Lord Voldemort's horrible Slytherin minions in today's Harry Potter books. Indian culture, conversely, deals with its fear of snakes by worshipping them, albeit from a safe distance. Our country is riddled with shrines and anthills dedicated to Nagaraj, the king of snakes. The logic of this is sound: if snakes are deified and fed and prayed to, they'll hopefully stay far, far away from us.

As always, science has a ready explanation for these fears. According to research carried out by a group of Swedish psychologists in 2001, the human brain may have been programmed by evolution to fear snakes. There was a time when our ancestors lived and foraged for food in a wilderness full of poisonous reptiles, and some of their fears may have carried over into our genes. Is this automatic genetic response to be fully trusted, though? Are snakes really as repugnant as we're wired to believe?

The only thing that makes me more nervous than snakes is the feeling that I'm not fully in control of my own mind. The way of science is to fully understand something before cultivating a response to it, and not to blindly follow the voices in your head. And so, in a practical experiment to try and reprogram my ophidiophobic brain, I accompanied my friends Narayan and KT on a trip into Agumbe, home of the world's largest venomous snake: the king cobra.

Agumbe is a little hamlet in Karnataka's Western Ghats, and it's famous for two reasons. It receives some of the highest rainfall in India (second only to Cherrapunji in Meghalaya), and it contains one of the rare field research stations in the country to encourage long-term monitoring of wildlife. Because of its weather and forests, Agumbe is home to a rich biodiversity (including a variety of snakes), which makes it an ideal place in which to observe wildlife. It was here, back in 1971, that the famed herpetologist and conservationist Romulus Whitaker saw his first king cobra in the wild. In 2005, Whitaker acquired four acres of rainforest-enveloped land in Agumbe, and used it to set up the Agumbe Rainforest Research Station (or ARRS). *(See box)*

> The ARRS may well be the best research station of its kind in India. It was partially modelled on the Smithsonian Tropical Research Institute (STRI), located in Barro Colorado Island in the Panama Canal Zone, which is considered to be the ideal research station by many biologists around the world. Like the STRI, the ARRS provides visiting researchers all the facilities they need for the long-term study of wildlife and biodiversity in a tropical rainforest. This kind of study is very important for conservation, because observing animals for long periods of time helps scientists understand their behaviour to the minutest degree.

All cover story photos are by Siddharth Rao, except where indicated otherwise

When Narayan, KT and I arrived at the ARRS, after a half day's drive down from Bangalore, the sky was clear and the air was dry. It was a hot, humid February, and the heavy rains were still some months away. Our chances of seeing wildlife would be much higher if it were raining, so this muggy weather was disappointing.

We were met at the station's wooden gates by Siddharth Rao, a conservation biologist and the Director of the station. "Welcome to ARRS!" he said. "You guys'll be staying at the Leopard Cottage."

"What a cool name. Why's it called that?" I asked.

"Because someone saw a leopard there. Hahaha."

I gulped.

"You guys can relax today. Walk around, hit the nature trail if you like, and generally get to know the place. Tomorrow you can go meet M4."

"What's M4?" asked KT.

"M4 is one of the king cobras we're tracking right now. The code 'M4' stands for 'male number

four'. He's been at the same burrow for a couple of days now, so this is a good time to visit him." *(See M4's home range on page 16)*

"Is it safe for us to go near the snake? Isn't the king cobra one of the most venomous snakes in the world?" asked Narayan.

"Yes, is it safe?" I echoed, nervously.

"He won't bother you if you don't bother him," said Siddharth. "That's how it is with most animals, you know. Don't worry. My colleague Dhiraj, who's been tracking M4, will accompany you. He'll call you tomorrow morning when the snake comes out to bask."

DAY 1

The next morning, just as we were winding up breakfast, Dhiraj called from a nearby village named Balehalli: M4's present location. The king cobra had found a burrow in a field next to an acacia and eucalyptus plantation. *(See box)*

> **Agumbe** has an added advantage for researchers studying king cobras, because it contains forests as well as fields and plantations. The general matrix of a king cobra's movement is heterogeneous. This means that it moves through forest patches, human habitations, plantations and paddy fields, that is wherever they can find food. Rodents that thrive around farms and fields are a favourite food of rat snakes, and king cobras in turn tend to eat rat snakes — so it's normal to find the cobras in farmed land. *(To find out what else king cobras eat, turn to page 15)*

Photo by Narayan Gopalan

Watch a short video about the Agumbe Rainforest Research Station at http://youtu.be/GOhOBKOe2Oc

Photo by Dhiraj Bhaisare

A king cobra munches on a spectacled cobra

had implanted a small battery-run radio transmitter.

"How did you manage to implant the transmitter inside the snake?" I asked.

"With some difficulty!" laughed Siddharth. "We had to first catch the cobra and sedate him. Then we performed a minor surgery on the animal in order to insert the transmitter under his skin. After we stitched him up and the snake had recovered from the surgery, we released him back into the wild." Siddharth had somehow managed to make it all sound quite matter-of-fact. If you want to appreciate how difficult this process really is though, all you have to do is imagine how a king cobra might react to being caught. *(See box)*

The three of us and Siddharth headed out to the location in the station's jeep. Dhiraj had been waiting outside M4's burrow since 9am. When he called us at 10.15am, the snake had just exited the burrow to bask in the Sun.

From the main road where we parked our jeep, we had to cross three fields, jump two electrified fences and a barbed wire fence, to get to where the cobra and its tracker patiently awaited us.

"King cobras don't travel around obstacles the way you and I do," explained Siddharth, as we gingerly climbed over a fence, taking great care not to graze our skins against its electrified wire. "They move across and through all kinds of terrain. That's what makes following them so difficult."

"So how do you keep track of them?" asked Narayan.

"We use a technology called radio telemetry. We're the first to use telemetry to track king cobras. You'll soon see it in action."

(To know more about how telemetry has helped the researchers at ARRS understand king cobras better, turn to page 15.)

When we arrived at the plantation, Dhiraj was ready with his telemetry gear. It consisted of a radio receiver, along with an antenna to catch the radio signal. The signal this equipment received came from under M4's skin, where the ARRS researchers

M4, for instance, is around 12 feet long, as wide as Arnold Schwarzenegger's forearms, incredibly strong and lightning-fast in movement. If he's cornered and thinks you're about to attack him, he'll rear up his head, growl and get ready to strike. The king cobra's striking range is roughly 7 feet — longer than the average star basketball player. Often, the king cobra's first strike will be a head-butt (no biting!), to warn you to stay clear of him. His second strike, if he's still not convinced that you present a real threat to him, may be a dry bite (without venom!). While a dry bite will scare most creatures away, it also helps the cobra conserve his venom, which takes his body a lot of time and resources to make. The final strike of the king cobra will be the death blow: he'll bite and inject huge, paralysing quantities of neurotoxins and cardiotoxins directly into your bloodstream. Unless you're lucky enough to have some anti-venom handy (which is highly unlikely given how little of it is manufactured in Indian labs), you'll be stone-dead within 15 minutes of being bitten. *Now* imagine catching a super-snake like M4 with just a tube, a stick and a bag, then sedating and performing surgery on him.

A king cobra rescue in progress:
King cobras often stray into human settlements. If conservationists don't get there in time to rescue the cobras, villagers take matters into their own hands and either beat the poor snakes to death or release them in some faraway place outside the snake's familiar home range *(go to page 16 to see how this kind of translocation affects the snakes).*

"How does your telemetry equipment work?" KT asked Dhiraj.

Dhiraj beckoned for us to come closer and listen to the radio receiver in his hand. "Do you hear that beeping sound? That's the signal from M4. It tells you what his heart rate is. If the beeps increase in frequency (frequency is the quickness of the beeps), it means the snake's body temperature is rising. And the louder the beeps are, the closer you are to the snake. Right now, we're a few metres away from the snake, so the beeps aren't too loud. The frequency of the beeps is around 30 beeps per minute (bpm), so he's still basking. If it gets to between 31 and 35, it means that the snake is either moving or that he's reached his optimal body temperature. Once that temperature is reached, he usually goes back into his burrow."

"How do you know for sure if he's moving?"

"If he's moving, the beeping pattern changes to a high-beep/low-beep alternation. Here, listen. It's quite steady, and just under 31bpm. It sounds like he's still basking."

Snakes like M4 are ectotherms, which means that they have to lie out in the Sun in order to increase their body temperature. When they've reached their optimal temperature, they have to retreat to a dark place from where to cool off. Mammals like us, on the other hand, are endotherms, meaning that we are able to regulate our own body temperature, regardless of our surroundings. If the outside temperature is cold, our bodies can warm themselves by shivering. If it's warm outside, we can cool down by sweating.

Watch Romulus Whitaker's TED Talk on reptile conservation, at:
http://youtu.be/vH99KFD-Bk8

"Listen to this!" said Dhiraj. "He's reached 32bpm! We'd better move! He's going to go back into the burrow any minute now!" Dhiraj extended the receiver's antenna in front of him, holding it parallel to the ground so that he could pick up the signal from M4 clearly. He then started jogging towards the burrow.

We followed him, breathless. We crunched over dead leaves and scrambled over a barbed wire fence towards a clump of dry bushes that Dhiraj pointed to. The burrow was a hole in the ground by the bushes.

"He's on the move!" whispered Dhiraj. "Try not to make too much noise! You don't want to scare the snake!"

We slowed down and tried to tread softly, but by the time we got to the burrow, it was too late. M4 had already disappeared inside. We eyed each other guiltily.

"You can come back again tomorrow," said Siddharth. "But only if you promise not to disturb the snake!"

DAY 2

Things weren't much better the next morning. M4 had started basking at 9.30am, and we arrived at the plantation by 9.45am. We were only a couple of metres away from the king cobra, when M4 reached 33bpm and started moving back into the burrow. We hurried over the barbed wire fence separating M4 and us, fraying our jeans on the barbs, and ran to the burrow. We got

5 Snake Myths That Had You Fooled

1. In the movies, if you get bitten by a poisonous snake, you can immediately cut the wound to extract the venom or suck the poison from the wound and spit it out.

In real life, cutting the wound caused by a snake bite is the worst thing you can do. It causes tissue damage and loss of blood. Sucking the venom out is another grave mistake. The venom spreads too fast for sucking to be of any help, and some of the venom ends up in your body as well.

2. Snakes drink milk.

Snakes don't drink milk. In fact, they can't even digest it properly. In times of dire thirst, and with no other option available, they may drink it. But it could be harmful to them and, quite possibly, may even kill them.

3. Snakes dislocate their jaws when swallowing animals whole.

Snakes possess several joints and their jaws are extremely flexible. This enables them to open their mouth very wide, and swallow their prey whole.

4. Snakes are aggressive and chase people.

Most snake species are shy creatures and avoid people. What is perceived as chasing may just be a snake hurrying to safety.

5. Some snakes are vegetarians.

Some snakes feed on rodents, others on larger animals and there are some that even feed on insects. But there is no such thing as a vegetarian snake.

(Compiled by Aparna Kapur)

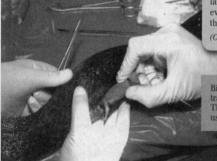

Biologists surgically implant a radio transmitter under the skin of a king cobra. This transmitter sends out a signal that is used to track the snake.

there just in time to see the lower half of the snake disappearing into the hole.

Dhiraj told us that M4 would come out to bask again in the afternoon. We decided to return then, and this time, in order to minimize our chances of disturbing M4, to try out a slightly different strategy.

We returned to the plantation at 3pm. M4 had only just gotten out to sun himself, so our chances of seeing him were high. Instead of approaching him directly over the fence like we'd been doing, though, we attempted a more circuitous route: by going around a couple of fields and arriving from a different direction altogether.

King cobras have an incredibly evolved sense of smell, which they perceive through their tongues. That's why they keep flicking their tongues in and out of their mouths — that's the way they sense their surroundings. We saw the whole of M4 for the first time when we were a couple of metres away from his burrow. He was coiled behind the bushes next to his burrow, his scales gleaming in the sunlight. We had only taken a few more steps forward when the wind changed direction and M4 suddenly sensed us coming.

He immediately started moving towards the burrow. We picked up our pace. And then we were there, directly in front of the burrow.

Just a few feet away from us, too close for comfort, M4 paused, reared up his head and looked straight at us. We froze. KT raised his camera, trying desperately to focus quickly for the money shot.

And just as suddenly, M4 was gone. He had decided that we weren't worth the trouble.

"Rats!" KT whispered. "I nearly had him!"

"It's okay, man," I said. "Forget the photo. We've just had an incredible life experience! We've seen a king cobra in the wild!"

"I know!" said KT. "How cool is that?"

On our wonderstruck drive back to the station, my friend Narayan asked me if I was still afraid of snakes.

I thought about it at length before replying. "I guess I am, a little," I said. "But you know what? I understand them better now. And I learned today that they're just as afraid of us as we are of them. That changes everything."

"How so?"

"Snakes don't seem evil any more, for one thing. M4 was so peaceful and reticent! He just wanted to be left alone so he could relax and do his thing."

"True," said KT. "If I were an endangered animal, being researched by some sneaky humans, I'd probably be just as shy. It's amazing that we got to see him!" ●

Dhiraj waits in the rain, tracking M4 through the forests of Agumbe with his radio telemetry equipment. He holds the receiver on his lap to listen to the king cobra's bpm reading. The receiver's antenna is kept perfectly parallel to the ground in order to receive the clearest-possible signal.

The ARRS' king cobra telemetry project has changed a lot of what we know about these snakes. Assisted by radio signals, the ARRS trackers have been studying the behaviour of king cobras for several years now, and this long-term monitoring has revealed several new facts.

NINE THINGS YOU DIDN'T KNOW ABOUT KING COBRAS (THAT WERE DISCOVERED USING RADIO TELEMETRY)

1. They like daytime: King cobras are mostly diurnal in habit (meaning, they roam around mostly in the daytime). They find their prey chiefly by olfactory and visual cues.

2. They move through human settlements: King cobra habitats might not be restricted to forests. They also periodically use farmland. However, their secretive nature results in very few interactions with people.

3. They climb trees: King cobras have often been observed climbing trees and foraging in them. They have also been seen predating on arboreal (tree-inhabiting) snake species like the Malabar Pit Viper (Trimeresurus malabaricus).

4. They like diving underwater: Although other terrestrial snakes are known to dive under water to take refuge, underwater foraging was a new behaviour in a wild king cobra that was observed for the first time by the telemetry project.

5. They have a strong homing instinct: Following the same snakes for almost a year each, revealed that they have a strong homing instinct. King cobras use the same burrows time and again for resting and shedding. Some burrows have been revisited by the same snakes even after six months.

6. They're scavengers: Although they are known to be active predators, the study has recorded, for the first time, a king cobra scavenging on the carcass of a three-foot long cat snake. The cat snake had been killed two days ago by villagers.

7. They forage at night: Most times, the king cobra retires to a refuge by sunset. But it has also been observed that when the snake has not been successful in capturing prey for a long duration, or is following a very strong scent trail, it continues to forage in darkness.

8. Mating season makes them travel: Male king cobras move considerable distances in search of mates. They often leave their home ranges to travel in search of females.

9. They don't take very kindly to being moved out of their home ranges: Snake translocation is common practice in India. The ill-effects of long-distance translocation were demonstrated by the differences in behaviour between the translocated and non-translocated king cobras. *(See box and following page)* ●

Forests are constantly being cut down to make space for the world's growing human population. One of the big problems with this is that wild animals often stray into villages and towns, because these inhabited areas once used to be part of the animal's home range. When stray king cobras are found in human settlements, they're caught and relocated somewhere far off, where they won't cause people any trouble. But this is usually worse, because the snake gets confused and starts looking for its old burrows and familiar places. In doing so, it ends up roaming over much larger areas than it used to. This only increases its chances of encountering humans again.

The map below shows the home ranges of three king cobras that were tracked by ARRS using radio telemetry. One of these snakes was translocated away from its home range *(turn to page 15 to know more about translocation)*. The black line represents M1's home range, the yellow line is M2's home range, and the red line is M4's. Can you identify the snake that was translocated? Write to us with your reasons at *brainwave@ack-media.com*. Two correct answers will each win a free six-month subscription to BRAINWAVE!

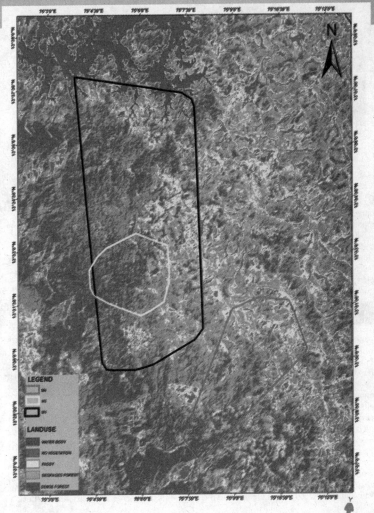

DEATHLY TALES OF VENOM

OF SNAKY EXPLOITS AND LETHAL PROTEINS

by **Samir Whitaker**

Besides being scary, snake venom is an incredibly fascinating and medically important mix of proteins. Venom is to snakes what saliva is to humans – an aid to feeding processes and digestion. There are a few major differences of course, including the fact that snakes can inject venom into their prey. And more importantly, our saliva probably couldn't kill anything!

FATAL FANGS

Venom, which has evolved over two hundred million years, is a hugely complex mixture of proteins and enzymes! Venoms can be classified into two groups based on their effects: neurotoxic and cytotoxic. Viper venom is typically cytotoxic i.e. it affects cells, while the venoms of cobras and kraits are mainly neurotoxic as they affect nerves and nerve impulses.

The ingredients of snake venoms work together in a variety of ways to make them effective and deadly. For example, snake venom contains an enzyme called hyaluronidase, which makes the tissue of the bitten animal more permeable – basically, this means that the tissue allows venom to be absorbed faster. Venoms can also hamper the flow of important enzymes such as cholinesterase, which makes the prey lose muscle control. And other fatal venoms can affect blood pressure.

POTENT PROTEINS

Believe it or not, the same proteins that cause these lethal effects can also help save lives. Several proteins in snake venom are already being used as painkillers and to treat blood coagulation (which leads to clots). Many more are currently being tested for human use. For instance, a particular protein in king cobra venom could soon become one of the most effective painkillers on the drug market.

VENOM VERSUS ANTIVENOM

It is equally important to come up with effective antivenom serum in the dire event of snakebites. Antivenom serum, the only sure way to treat a serious bite from a venomous snake, was first made against cobra venom in 1904. The techniques used to produce it haven't changed a whole lot since. Most of the world's antivenom is made by injecting horses or sheep with very tiny

SAW-SCALED VIPER'S VENOM BEING EXTRACTED HERE.

Photos courtesy: Romulus Whitaker

OH, CMON. BITE IT.

TIC...TIC...

ANTI VENOM

Artwork: Somesh Kumar

quantities of snake venom. The horse then produces antibodies against the venom, which cause the venom molecules to be destroyed. These can be purified and used to save human lives. Luckily for us, antibodies produced by other species work well when injected into humans.

But wait – there is a twist in this snaky story. The science of snake venom is further complicated by an interesting fact – the venom of the same species (for example, the Indian cobra or Naja naja) can be very different from one part of India to another. Exactly how different? Studies have shown that antivenom serum made from the venom of the Naja naja in one part of India did not neutralise Naja naja venom from other parts of the country. Basically, if you have been bitten by a cobra in Bhopal, antivenom made using the venom of a cobra from Kerala may not save you. Scary!

This geographic variation in Indian snake venom is the focus of a new research project being conducted by scientists from the Madras Crocodile Bank, the Indian Institute of Science and the University of Mysore. The project hopes to provide information that will help antivenom manufacturers make their products more effective. The ultimate cure for snakebites in India will be antivenom serum made with snake venoms from different parts of the country, one that will be equally effective in all parts of India.

Samir Whitaker is the Assistant Director of Madras Crocodile Bank, one of the largest reptile zoos in the world.

73

SNAKES AND TORCHES

❖ OPPONENT - THE BIG FOUR   ❖ MAP - TEA PLANTATION

>> INDIAN
SPECTACLED COBRA

>> COMMON KRAIT

>> RUSSELL'S VIPER

>> SAW-SCALED VIPER

PLAYER 01
SPECIAL POWER - NIL

The 'Big Four' are the most dangerous species of venomous snakes in India.

Since they feed mainly on common rodents, these snakes are drawn to human-populated areas. Between them, they cause a majority of the snake-related deaths in this country.

Deadly as they are, though, the 'Big Four' are also extremely shy. They are known to attack only if they are provoked or when they feel threatened. Their shyness, combined with their largely nocturnal habits, make them very easy to miss.

If you live near fields, plantations or places with lots of tree-cover, it is important to be alert and on the look-out for these snakes, especially after dark. All the experts recommend that you make sure to carry a torch at all times.

PLAYER 02
SPECIAL POWER - TORCH

TREE-SPIRITED

by Veena Prasad

DOWN

1. ___system, or biome (3)
2. Forests at high altitude having stunted vegetation are called ____ forests (5)
3. Tree found in deciduous forests (5)
4. Coniferous trees largely make up this biome (5)
6. Number of seed-leaves in a monocot (3)
7. Dendrochronology involves counting a tree's annual ___ (5)
8. ___'s viper: A rare snake in the cloud mountains of the Himalayas (3)
9. Fruit-eating animals help in dispersing a tree's ____ (5)
11. A cobra's flexible ____ makes it possible for it to swallow food larger than its head (3)
13. Acorns grow on this tree (3)

ACROSS

2. Not sparse (5)
5. A cloud forest in this desert country thrives on moisture from low lying clouds (4)
6. ___vore: organisms that eat both plants and animals (4)
7. The world's largest flower; grows in the rainforests of Indonesia (9)
10. Genus to which most cobras (except king cobras) belong (4)
12. ____phyte: A plant that grows in extremely dry areas (4)
14. One is usually advised not to miss these for the trees (5)

Send us your completed crosswords, and give us your feedback! Write to *brainwave@ack-media.com*.

GURGLINGS OF OOPS

The distance between galaxies is much more than the distance between stars.

But there are some galaxies which are closer to earth even than the center of our own galaxy, the Milky Way.

The closest galaxy to us is a dwarf galaxy called Canis Major which is 25,000 light years away from Earth. It is called a dwarf galaxy because it is relatively small.

The Milky Way has between 200 and 400 billion stars. Canis Major on the other hand has only about a billion stars.

Oops does not like the term dwarf, because humans usually make fun of him, calling him dwarf or shorty. According to him, Canis Major is a 'cute' galaxy and not a dwarf galaxy.

The nearest spiral galaxy to the Milky Way is the Andromeda galaxy, about 2.5 million light years away from our galaxy. It is on a collision course with our galaxy, rushing towards us at about 110 kilometer per second. It will collide with the Milky Way in about five billion years.

The most widely agreed upon estimate for the age of the Universe is 13.77 billion years. The current belief about the size of the Universe is that it is at least 93 billion light-years across. So the Universe is 93 billion times 9,500,000,000,000 kilometers across! Oops once calculated this. There were so many zeros in the calculation that he exclaimed in Gurglese—'odam itisroun danroun danround,' which in English means 'It looks like rows and rows of baby gurgles.' There are at least around 176 billion galaxies in the observable universe.

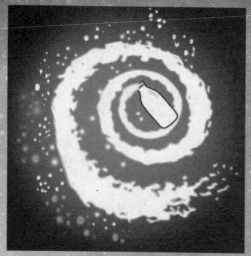

The Milky Way is called such because of it's white colour. Not because if is made out of milk!

This number has been arrived at based on the limited technology available today.

It is possible that actually there are more than a trillion galaxies, each with close to 100 billion stars.

The Gurglings of Oops on the Universe is, 'Megawd meheadis pinningands pin ingat thetho tofit. Aifeel sov erysma landstupid.'

Translation in English —'The Universe is such an awe-inspiring and incredible place, but gurgles are masters of the universe and for the gurgles, the whole universe is like their backyard.'

The Universe is also expanding—the current belief is that this rate of expansion is increasing. This increasingly faster expansion is attributed to 'dark energy', a form of energy which has not been identified as of now. There is also proof for the existence of 'dark matter' a type of matter that cannot be detected using current technology. While dark matter increases the overall gravitational pull of the universe and tries to reduce the speed of expansion, dark energy increases the rate of expansion. Together, dark energy and dark matter contribute to about 95% of the Universe.

Oops and his friends Chuck and Kia discovered that the mysterious invisible creatures from the dark planets, Solarcel and Fotosynthesis are able to harness dark energy and hence have great power. They even gifted Oops, Chuck and Kia with bamboozlers which are powerful gadgets. They are controlled by thought, can shrink a person, freeze a person, help a person fly and even invisibly scratch a person's back.

It is believed that the Universe began as an extremely dense and hot point, less than the size of an atom. In the first 10-32 seconds, it expanded to about 100 million light years across. This is referred to as inflation. The matter in the Universe was not evenly distributed and there were parts which were denser than others. These denser parts became stars. It took around 750 million years for the first stars to form.

Even in Oops's time—millions of years in our future, no one has travelled to other galaxies. According to Oops, the worms which have been genetically modified to eat up space-time and create wormholes are not hungry enough to eat through the distance between galaxies. Oops believes that Gurgles will be the first to invent worms who are famished enough to create intergalactic jumps.

SHIKARI SHAMBU

THE SSSUMMER GUESSST

Story & Script Anisha H. Karthick   **Pencils and Inks** Savio Mascarenhas   **Colours** Umesh & Akshay   **Letters** Pranay Bendre

81

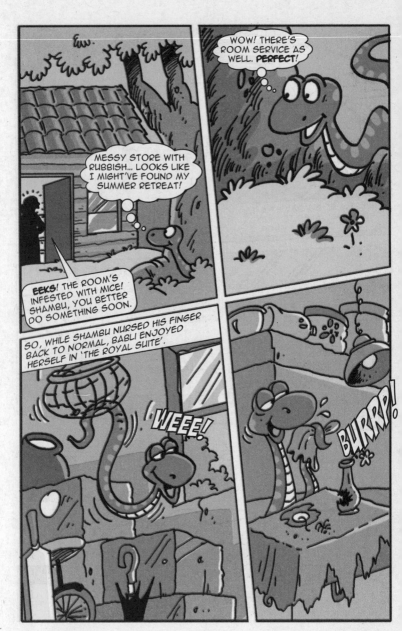

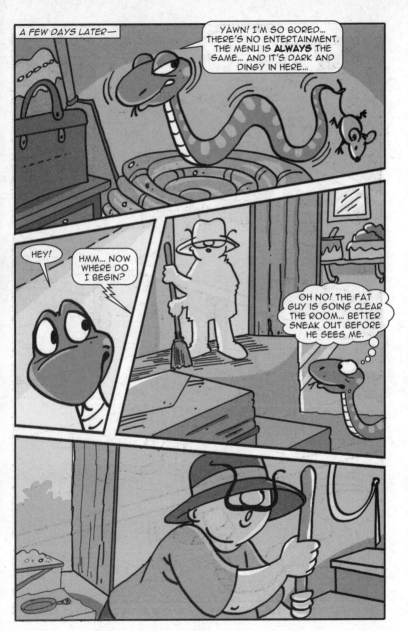

83

84

BABLI ENTERED THE BEDROOM, AND SHE WAS REALLY IMPRESSED WITH THE AMBIENCE INSIDE.

86

87

88

With the holidays on, I am sure you kids are playing lots of games, both real and virtual (although I hope that most of you play outdoors!). Recently my grandniece showed me an online game which was very interesting, even for someone of my age. Now, I am sure you must think that a grand old lady like me could never appreciate video games. But I beg to differ! This particular game is called 'paper dolls', and indeed it is the online version of the game that I used to play as a child with real paper dolls!

An example of early paper dolls.

Paper Dolls have been around for as long as there has been paper, and are a fun way for children to make shapes or play dress-up with their favourite characters. A basic technique in making a paper doll is Japanese Origami, practiced as early as 800 AD. A colourful piece of paper is folded to create a human-like shape or a kimono, among other things. I am sure you have done some of this craft as part of your school projects. The more modern form of a paper doll in comparison is a thin cardboard cut-out which comes with several clothing pieces made of paper cut-outs, that one can clip on to the original figure. As a young girl, I remember playing with my Cinderella paper doll for several hours. It came with two changeable dresses, two cut-outs of shoes and also a crown.

Modern paper dolls first emerged in the West in the mid-18th century and were initially created for adults, with dolls dressed in the fashions of that time. French versions of these early paper dolls can be found in museums across Europe and date back to the 1780s. As the popularity of the paper dolls grew, they were used for commercial purposes, usually advertising a product such as clothing, or to promote a celebrity or movie star.

This trend was especially popular in the USA. Book publishing companies soon followed suit. Originals of these paper dolls, most of which were meticulously hand painted, are now considered antique and sell for high prices.

Fans and collectors of paper dolls hold conventions and exhibitions throughout the year in several parts of the world. The most famous among them is the International Paper Doll Convention, which takes place in the USA every year. Participants can create their own paper dolls in costumes of their choice, which they may put on sale during the event. If you would like to find out more about paper dolls, you can visit *http://paperstudiopress.com/* Happy holidays and keep on playing!

Early paper dolls would exhibit the fashions of the time

MAKE YOUR OWN PAPER DOLL!

DRESS YOUR DOLL BY CUTTING OUT THESE OUTFITS AND HAIRSTYLES!

FOLD THESE BITS TO FIX THE OUTFIT ON THE DOLL

94

THAT NIGHT, AMAR TOLD HIS PARENTS ABOUT THE CONCERT –

HMM...IT WOULD DO YOU KIDS GOOD TO LISTEN TO CLASSICAL MUSIC. WE NEVER HAD SUCH OPPORTUNITIES WHEN I WAS IN SCHOOL !

OH, YOU CAN COME WITH ME, DAD !

PRINCI SAID PARENTS WERE INVITED TOO !

EEP!! HOW...ER... THOUGHTFUL OF HIM...

B...BUT I'LL BE WORKING LATE THAT DAY ! WHY DON'T YOU GO, DEAR ?

NO, THANKS ! YOU TWO AREN'T DRAGGING ME INTO THIS !

LATER THAT NIGHT –

I CAN'T BELIEVE BOTH MA AND DAD WRIGGLED OUT OF THIS CONCERT ! IF ONLY I COULD TOO !

SUDDENLY –

aaaaa! oooo !

WHAT'S THAT AWFUL NOISE ?!!

aaaaaa!

AARGH ! I CAN'T TAKE IT ANYMORE !

99

FINALLY –

AMAR! STOP THAT INFERNAL NOISE! MR. GOVIND IS HERE... AND HE HAS SOMETHING HE WANTS TO SAY TO YOU!

EEEEP!

YOU CHASED THE MUSICIANS AWAY FROM MY HOUSE! THEY SAID THE TORTUROUS NOISES NEXT DOOR WERE TOO MUCH FOR THEIR SENSITIVE SOULS TO BEAR!

I...I'M SO SORRY...

NOT AT ALL! NEVER HAD A MOMENT'S PEACE WHEN THEY WERE HERE! THEY MADE A REAL RACKET AND I'M GLAD THEY'RE GONE!

OH, GOOD!

NOW IF ONLY YOU PROMISE TO STOP PLAYING TOO, PEACE WILL BE RESTORED IN OUR NEIGHBOURHOOD!

ERR...

IN TROUBLE AGAIN, BUTTERFINGERS?!

RUSSELL! THE LEAD SINGER OF THE HEEBIE JEEBIES! WHAT ARE **YOU** DOING **HERE**?

WE GOT A CALL FROM YOUR PRINCIPAL! HE SAID YOUR CLASSICAL CONCERT WILL HAVE TO BE CANCELLED BECAUSE THE MUSICIANS RAN AWAY....

UH-OH!

101

THEN YOUR PRINCI VERY POLITELY ASKED US TO FILL IN FOR THEM IF WE COULD!

SO THE HEEBIE JEEBIES WILL PLAY AT THE CONCERT?! AWESOME!

I'M SORRY, BUTTER, IT'S IMPOSSIBLE! THAT'S WHY I CAME TO TALK TO YOU SO YOU COULD TELL THE OTHER KIDS TOO.

B...BUT... WHY NOT?!

MY GUITAR IS BEING RESTRUNG AND MY BACKUP ISN'T WORKING. WE JUST CAN'T GET ANOTHER DECENT ELECTRIC GUITAR ON SUCH SHORT NOTICE...

...YOU MEAN LIKE THIS ONE?!

H...H...HOW DID YOU...

...IT'S A LONG STORY! JUST DEDICATE A SPECIAL SONG TO A GUY CALLED 'ERIC' WHEN YOU PLAY! IT'S HIS GUITAR!

AND SO THAT NIGHT, THE HEEBIE JEEBIES PERFORMED —

HEY! TONIGHT WE'RE GOING TO PLAY SOME CLASSIC SONGS TOO AS A SPECIAL REQUEST!

AS THE ENTIRE SCHOOL BOPPED ALONG TO THE BEAT —

I GUESS ALL KINDS OF MUSIC ARE ENJOYABLE!

YOU SAID IT, SIR!

Theft at Naveen Villa

Inspector Sharpe arrived at Naveen Villa, the home of the businessman, Mr. Lotpot. The bungalow had been burgled while Mr. Lotpot and his wife were away on a world tour. The only person at home was Mr. Moppat, Mr. Lotpot's nephew.

"I'd been out shopping," said Mr. Moppat. "When I returned, I'd just turned the key in the lock when I was accosted at gunpoint by a masked man."

"Can you describe him?" asked Inspector Sharpe as he examined the empty cupboard.

"All I could make out was that he was tall and thin," replied Mr. Moppat.

"All right, go on with your story," encouraged the Inspector.

"Well, the fellow tied me up and gagged me. He then forced open the cupboard and took everything in the safe."

"Do you have any idea how much money or valuables were taken?"

"Uncle usually keeps about 3-4 lakh in cash in the safe plus some of my aunt's jewellery. Anyway, I realised the robber had left when I heard the front door click shut behind him. I struggled against my bonds but could only manage to get the gag off. I cried out for help and was luckily heard by a man passing by outside. He came in, untied me and I immediately called the police."

"Do you know the man who came to your help?" asked Inspector Sharpe.

"No, I've never seen him before and he disappeared soon after I thanked him!" replied Mr. Moppat.

"Well, that solves the case!" said Inspector Sharpe.

How did Inspector Sharpe solve the case?

Answer to You Be The Detective 573: Mr. Moppat said he heard the door click shut when the robber left, yet the passer-by could just walk into the house and untie him. Clearly Mr. Moppat is lying and is the thief. He just created the burglary story to avert suspicion.

Rhythm

IN ORDER TO SUCCEED

If you want to succeed in life,
Always keep trying again!
Though many times you may fail,
Always keep trying again!
If you fall on the ground,
Keep trying once again,
Never ever lose hope,
But always try again.
If you want to reach the top of the hill,
Always try again,
Though many times you may slip and fall,
But always try again.
Though you may have to face obstacles,
Always try again,
Coz they're the stepping stones to success,
So just keep on trying again.

- Vee Kay (Vanicia Kharsahnoh),
Jowai, Meghalaya

THE MIGHTY MAGNET

I am a mighty magnet,
And am very strong,
But if you use me exactly right,
Nothing can go wrong.
I can pick up objects,
But not everything you see,
I only pick up things,
That are attracted to me.
So take me now,
And try me out,
And you will quickly see,
What different kind of things,
Are pulled by me.
How do you know,
Which way to go,
Look at me,
And I will show.
North, South, East or West,
For finding direction,
I am the best.

- S. K. Uma, Kolkata.

& Hues

Aditya Darekar,
Kuwait.

Vinaya, Karimnagar,
Andhra Pradesh.

FRIENDSHIP

Friendship is a happy experience,
It makes us laugh,
And it makes us cry.
It makes us sing,
It makes us seek,
It makes us weep,
And above all,
It makes us live.

- **Purva Karmarkar**, Goregaon, Mumbai

POSERS

These are some of the other creatures that have been spotted at Agumbe *(clockwise from left)*: A bicoloured frog; a Malabar pit viper waits in readiness to strike; a rowdy gang of human researchers hanging out at a meadow next to the Agumbe Rainforest Research Station; the beta-carboline in a scorpion's shell makes it glow when ultraviolet light is shone on it; a tarantula prepares to enter its nest; and a draco lizard chills out on a branch.

Photo of Malabar pit viper by
Narayan Gopalan; photo of ARRS
team by Chetana Purushotham; all
remaining photos by Siddharth Rao

BIRDS IN TREES

Devised by **Siddharth Rao**

Your secret mission, Young Wildlifer, if you choose to accept it, is to find out how important fruiting trees are in maintaining bird diversity in cities and towns.

You will need:

Binoculars (minimum 7 x 40) ● A bird book (we recommend *The Book of Indian Birds* by Salim Ali, Oxford University Press) ● A field notebook and a pen ● Access to a computer

Artwork: Somesh Kumar

What to do:

● First, find a fruiting tree in your neighbourhood: e.g., a mango tree or a guava tree.

● Download the initial data sheet for this study (beginbirding.pdf) from **www.brainwavemagazine.com/birdstudy.php**, print it out and carry it with you.

● Once a week, spend one hour (either early in the morning between 7am and 8am, or in the late evening between 4pm and 5pm) observing the activity on your chosen tree. Note down the number and types of birds that visit the tree, during this one hour period.

● Data should be recorded at 10 minute intervals. For example, at 07:00, you note the number and type of birds and their activity. You must do this again at 07:10, 07:20, 07:30 and so on (for six times in one hour). If you run out of data sheets, print extra copies.

● Do this for four months: for two months when the tree has ripe fruit, and for another two months when the tree doesn't have fruits in it.

● At the end of four months, go back to **www.brainwavemagazine.com/birdstudy.php** and download the final data sheet (endbirding.xls). Find and collect everything that you jotted into your initial data sheets over four months. Type your findings into the final data sheet, and mail it to *brainwave@ack-media.com*. Our crack team of biologists will then show you how to analyse your data, and help you figure out what it all means.

B\W COMICS PRESENTS

THE MESSAGE FROM ARISTARCHUS

EPISODE 2: ALOK

SCRIPT BY SHALINI SRINIVASAN \ ARTWORK BY RAJIV EIPE
BASED ON A NOVEL OF THE SAME NAME BY DR. JAYANT NARLIKAR

Previously: Working secretly and illegally at the Cyclops facility in 1985, John Pringle searches for life in outer space.

But he arouses the suspicions of the military.

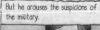

November 4th, 2025, 40 years later, Maharashtra, India. Malini and Sudhakar Naik were driving to Karad.

TAKE THAT TURN. LET'S GET OFF THE HIGHWAY.

AN ACCIDENT?

IN THIS DAY AND AGE!

WHO WOULD ABANDON THEIR CHILD IN THE MIDDLE OF THE ROAD?

WAAAAAH!

And so Alok found a home.

The Naiks soon realised that Alok was extremely intelligent. When he was three, their friend Dr. Salunke visited them.

I HAVE JIGSAW PUZZLES FOR YOU ALOK. SUDHAKAR, MALINI, I GOT YOU A RUBIK'S CUBE. YOU HAVE TO MOVE THESE BLOCKS SO THAT EACH SIDE HAS BLOCKS OF ONLY ONE COLOUR. IT'S HARDER THAN IT LOOKS!

TEA'S READY!

While the adults exchanged their news, Alok tried out the new puzzles.

I FINISHED THEM ALL, MA. I'M GOING TO MY ROOM, NOW.

SUDHAKAR, DID YOU ...

SOLVE THE CUBE? NO.

BUT I DIDN'T EITHER. THAT MEANS ...

... ALOK SOLVED IT! THAT'S IMPOSSIBLE!

One day, when Alok was about five, he was at a classmate's birthday party.

RING A RING O' ROSES
A POCKET FULL OF POSIES
A-TISHOO! A-TISHOO!
WE ALL FALL ...

...DOWN!

DID THEY REALLY DIE? WHY DID THEY ALL FALL?

IT'S OK, ALOK, THEY'RE FINE.

HA HA HEE

As soon as Alok was in bed that night, Malini told Sudhakar the story.

THAT'S JUST VERY INTELLIGENT OF HIM. THAT POEM IS ABOUT PEOPLE DYING DURING THE PLAGUE, YOU KNOW.

Sudhakar bought Alok a small telescope, and soon Alok was obsessed with astronomy.

HE'S ALWAYS SITTING ALONE IN THE DARK NOW! HE NEVER PLAYS WITH THE OTHER CHILDREN.

HE SEEMS HAPPY. OTHER PARENTS WOULD KILL TO HAVE A CHILD WHO STUDIES FOR FUN. HE KNOWS MORE MATHS THAN MOST FIFTEEN YEAR OLDS.

When Alok was 10, his maths teacher, Mr Mishra asked him to write the tests for the World Talent Search.

YOU'RE ALREADY THE TOP STUDENT IN OUR SCHOOL. IF YOU DO WELL IN THESE TESTS YOU MAY GET TO TAKE A TRIP TO THE MOON.

Alok topped the exam.

And so Alok found himself standing in a space shuttle, waiting for take off.

HI, I'M SANDRA. YOU'RE ALOK NAIK, RIGHT? I HEARD YOU TOPPED THE EXAM?

I HATE TO ADMIT IT, BUT I'M A LITTLE SCARED. ARE YOU?

10, 9...

6, 5...

3, 2, 1...

This is the Andaman Nightjar, a rare nocturnal bird that is endemic to certain parts of the Andaman and Nicobar Islands. Added to the fact that it comes out only at night, this nightjar is also extremely shy, because of which it has never been photographed before. Until this March, that is, when a group of wildlife biology students from Bangalore's National Centre for Biological Sciences (NCBS) visited the Andaman and Nicobar Islands Environmental Team (ANET), a research station set up by the same people responsible for the Agumbe Rainforest Research Station. While trekking through the forests of Redskin Island (which is part of the Mahatma Gandhi Marine National Park), one of these students, Shashank Dalvi, looked up and saw the most unlikely sight: an Andaman nightjar out in the daytime! The lucky shot that Dalvi clicked then was the first time this bird has ever been photographed. And what you're looking at now is the first instance — EVER! — that an image of the Andaman nightjar has been captured in print!

Photo courtesy: Shashank Dalvi

A BRAINWAVE exclusive!

a Light Bulb moment !

Artwork: Somesh Kumar

by **Aparna Kapur**

Snake attacks in villages are significantly higher when compared to those in cities. A major cause for this is inadequate lighting in rural areas. The lack of well-lit streets in villages also restricts movement. Come nightfall and villagers hesitate to step out of their homes for fear of an unexpected encounter with a snake.

The solution to this tricky problem is simple — well-lit villages. If villages could manage to find ways to generate sufficient light, the threat of prowling nocturnal creatures would reduce drastically. One bright idea is to use solar-powered LEDs or 'Light Emitting Diodes'. These eco-friendly lighting products, including bulbs, lamps and lanterns, harness the Sun's energy to give out light that is both affordable and energy-efficient.

A few visionary organisations have made it their business to take this innovative technology to these homes and light up the lives of people, quite literally. "Typically, people in villages use kerosene lamps, which are not only expensive and inefficient, but also harmful to health," says Anish Thakkar, co-founder and Global Marketing Manager of Greenlight Planet. This United States-based company has recently launched a solar home light, 'Sun King', which emits up to 16 hours of light after charging in the Sun for a day.

There are several other companies like InnovLite, D.light and Selco that are also addressing lighting needs using solar-powered LEDs. Mandeep Singh, Chief Operating Officer (India) of D.light, says, "What makes our products special is that they are extremely easy to use. And they provide white, bright light as opposed to the yellow dingy light from kerosene lamps. It is a much better option." ●

Photos courtesy: Greenlight Planet

SUBSCRIBE NOW!

	TINKLE MAGAZINE		TINKLE DIGEST		TINKLE COMBO MAGAZINE + DIGEST	
	1 yr subscription	2 yr subscription	1 yr subscription	2 yr subscription	1 yr subscription	2 yr subscription
	Pay only ₹480 ₹380!	Pay only ₹960 ₹750!	Pay only ₹720 ₹580!	Pay only ₹1440 ₹1080!	Pay only ₹1200 ₹880!	Pay only ₹2400 ₹1680!

I would like a subscription for

TINKLE MAGAZINE | **TINKLE COMBO** | **TINKLE DIGEST**
☐ 1 yr | ☐ 2 yrs   ☐ 1 yr | ☐ 2 yrs   ☐ 1 yr | ☐ 2 yrs

(Please tick the appropriate box)

YOUR DETAILS*

Name: .... Date of Birth: |__|__| / |__|__| / |__|__|

Address: ....

.... City: .... Pin: |__|__|__|__|__|__| State: ....

School: .... Class: ....

Tel: .... Mobile: +91 - |__|__|__|__|__|__|__|__|__|__|

Email: .... Signature: ....

PAYMENT OPTIONS

☐ Cheque /DD:

Please enclose Cheque /DD no. |__|__|__|__|__|__| drawn in favour of 'ACK Media Direct Ltd.'

at .... (bank) for the amount ....

dated |__|__| / |__|__| / |__|__|__|__| and send it to: IBH Books & Magazines Distributers Pvt. Ltd., Arch No. 30, West Approach, Below Mahalaxmi Bridge, Mahalaxmi (W), Mumbai - 400034.

☐ Pay Cash on Delivery: Pay cash on delivery of the first issue to the postman. (Additional charge of ₹50 applicable

☐ Pay by money order: Pay by money order in favour of "ACK Media Direct Ltd."

☐ Online subscription: Please visit: www.amarchitrakatha.com

For any queries or further information: Email: customerservice@ack-media.com or Call: 022-40497435 / 36

Subbu Soup

Story: Shriya Ghate   Art: Archana Amberkar

List 1: Ways to make Mum feel better:

1. Make funny Jokes.
2. Imitate a Baboon
3. Sing a Song

' Flop, flop, flop,' said Nishi as she scratched away at the list.

For the last couple of days, Nishi's mum had been staying more and more in bed and less and less at the office. Nishi had tried many things to make her feel better, but unfortunately none of them had worked. Mum was still quite sick and nothing Nishi did could get her out. Without Mum for company, she had no one to talk to and this made Nishi bored and sad.

To pass her time Nishi would watch TV, but as soon as her darling *Kazukai the Ninja Warrior* cartoon would come on, their neighbour, the annoying Laji Auntie, would somehow manage to catch her.

Just this morning, she had plastered her thick rimmed owl-like glasses against the window and pressed her stubby fingers on the pane making ten white spots.

'Is Nishi doing her homework and being the best girl she can be?' she had asked in her screechy sing-song voice. Quickly Nishi had switched off the TV, grabbed a book, flopped herself on the sofa and smiled a good-girl smile.

'Yes Laji Auntie,' she had replied in an equally sing-song voice.

'Don't forget! While your Mum is in bed, I am going to keep a strict eye on you...' Laji Aunty had said, and then her eyes had darted so wildly from side to side, Nishi thought they would pop out of their sockets at any moment.

What a buggidy bore and eyesore, thought Nishi. If this went on for any longer, she would surely lose her mind. There had to be something she could do to make Mum all right again.

***

Pacing the courtyard of their house now, Nishi kept her eyes tight shut. She had seen Kazukai do this before on TV, so she knew that the tighter you squeezed your eyes, the faster the ideas would come.

Bzzz. Bzzz.

But nothing happened. She tried again, this time squatting on the lawn.

Bzzz.

Just as she was concentrating, Nishi felt something on her knee. It was wet and tickly. It had to be Subbubee!

Subbu or Subbubee, as Nishi called him, was the neighbourhood stray dog and her only friend in the apartment building. They had known each other from the time Nishi was two feet tall, and Subbu a wobbly foot-high puppy.

Opening her eyes, she saw Subbu busily licking something from a throw-away plastic cup. For as long as she could remember, Subbu had a habit of picking things off the road.

'Bad Subbu! How many times have I told you not to eat that stuff!' she said stroking his head and pulling his ears.

Slober, slober, slober. He was too busy eating to respond.

She bent over Subbu to look into the container. It looked like soup. As Subbu licked away furiously, something began to whirr in Nishi's mind.

Bzzzz. Bzzzzzzz.

She shut her eyes tight again.

Bzzzzzzzzzzz.

Bzzzzzzzzzzzzzzzzzzzzzzzzzzzzzz

'SOUP!' cried Nishi, opening her eyes.

'Woof!' barked Subbu.

'That's it! That's it, Subbu,' she said patting his back, 'We are going to make Mum some soup. Wait till she finds out it was you who gave me the idea!'

***

Nishi tip-toed into the kitchen. She was using Kazukai's Double 'S' Ninja technique of SILENCE and SPEED, especially since there was no knowing when nosy Laji Aunty would pop by.

Nishi had never made soup before, but she had watched Mum do it countless times, and remembered it to the last detail:

Take a pot. Throw in the multicoloured powders. Wait for the firecracker-like splatter and sizzle. Dump the gross vegetables in the pot. Pour some water or milk. And then stir and stir till the liquid boiled and blistered and bubbled like lava.

Fetching a pen and paper, as she had often seen Mum do, she made a rough list of what she would put in her soup. Then one by one, she started gathering the ingredients on the counter, ticking them off as she found them.

Milk ✓
Raw eggs ✓
Salt ✓
Splattering powders

'Mmm...where are the powders?'

As she bent to look for them, something tugged at her dress. She turned around to find Subbu chewing away at the end of her frock. In her hurry, she had forgotten to close the front door and Subbu had followed her in.

She was so shocked to see him that she accidently banged her head on the cabinet door.

'Ouch! Silly Dog!', she said, pushing him, 'You are not allowed in this house! Go! Shoo! Can't you see I'm busy?'

She banged her foot at Subbu threateningly, but he sprang away and scampered off in another direction.

'No no no no noooooooo...'

But it was too late. Subbu had smelled something yummy in the fridge and was barking and yelping for Nishi to give him some.

'Quiet, you fool! You'll wake Mum up. God! I'm going to get into so much trouble.'

Opening the fridge slightly, she brought out a slice of chicken salami and held it out to him. He lunged for it, but Nishi ducked, turned around and ran out the front door. Subbu followed, jumping and wagging his tail. Just as soon as they were outside, she quickly dropped the slice to the floor, rushed inside and slammed it shut.

'Haha. Stupid dumbo!' she said, sticking out her tongue at him, 'Phew... Now, back to the soup.'

***

Nishi found her mother's magic steel box of splattering and sizzling powders in the spice cabinet. Moving it around, she heard a clinking sound. She held it tightly with one arm and pulled hard at the lid with the other.

The lid released itself centimeter by centimeter until finally it opened with a *WHOOM*. The trapped smells of spices rushed out like genies from lamps.

Accchooo!
She sneezed as they tickled the inside of her nose.

Inside the big steel box were several small round boxes. Inside each tiny round box was a different coloured powder and each powder had a different smell. Nishi breathed them in one by one, and as their aromas mingled, they made her stomach rumble with hunger.

All the ingredients gathered it was now time to make the soup. But before she could begin, she would need a large pot. Unfortunately, the pot she wanted was high up in a cabinet over her head. She had to lean all the way back to get a good look at it. 'Whew! That's highly dangerous,' she thought, and rubbed her hands in delight.

Climbing the tall rickety stool, she carefully put her feet on the top, one by one. Spacing them evenly to get her balance, she held out her arms like an airplane, and breathed in deeply. This was the Kazukai Meditation Before Battle Technique.

In the cave of the cabinet, the massive upturned pot looked like a giant asleep on its stomach. A circular handle stuck out from the side. Nishi put her fingers around it and flexed them to make sure

she had a good grip. And then she began pulling.

Screech. Screech. Screech.

With her eyebrows crossed, she was concentrating so hard it was making her forehead sweat. She slid the pot out of the shelf until the other handle was visible.

Huff. Puff.

Gripping the second handle with her other hand, she hoisted it up with a single sweep, like a trophy. Hurray!

Back on the ground, Nishi put the pot on the stove. But where was the fire? Mum had always told her not to light it herself. 'Only when you're grown up!', her Mum used to say. But Mum wasn't here now, and Nishi had no choice but to do it herself. Taking the T-shaped lighter in hand, she held it up in the air like a gun.

Click. Click.

It seemed to be fine. Turning a chocolate brown knob on the hob, she pointed the lighter to the burner.

Click. Click. Nothing happened.

She tried again.

'Foooo!' Nothing.

'Eeeya!' Nothing.

'Kazukai!'

At once, the stove lit up and blue flames erupted from the burner. Half an hour later, strong rancid smells flowed out of the kitchen. In fact, the smells were so strong that even Subbu, who was outside, could smell them. Nishi could hear him barking and scratching the front door.

In the pot, a thick yellow-green liquid was frothing away. Standing on her toes, she stared into it, stirring it once with her right hand and then with her left.

'That surely ought to get Mum out of bed,' she thought, as a whale-sized smile appeared on her face.

***

Mum was fast asleep when Nishi entered the bedroom. She got

under the blanket and snuggled next to her.

'Ooh... you're burning!' she said, rubbing her head on
Mum's shoulder.

Mum opened her heavy eyes, smiled and kissed Nishi on the head.

'Mum....,' said Nishi.

'Hmm?'

'I've been making...'

'Hmm...'

'I have a surprise for you, Mum!'

Mum's eyes were now fully open.

'Really? Did you do all your homework by your self?'

'No! Of course not!'

'Then?'

'Close your eyes,' said Nishi.

'What?'

'It's a surprise! Close your eyes!'

Nishi ran back to the kitchen. In a minute, she was back carrying a
bowl of soup on a wobbly tray.

'Can I open my eyes now?' said Mum.

'Not yet! Don't look!'

'What's that smell?'

Nishi carefully placed the tray on the bed side table.

'Now!'

Mum opened her eyes and sniffed. 'What's that smell?' she said bewildered. 'Beside you! Look beside you.' Mum turned to her side. With a giddy head and fuzzy eyes, it took her a few seconds to realise it was a steaming bowl of soup. She sat up suddenly.

'It worked!' cackled Nishi.

'What's this?' cried Mum.

Nishi carefully lifted the tray and placed it on Mum's lap.

'What do you think?'

'You turned on the stove yourself?' Mum asked, half-angry and half-worried.

'Yeah,' replied Nishi sheepishly.

'I told you not to touch it!'

'Sorry Mum.'

'Did you turn it off?'

'Yes, Mum.'

'Are you sure?'

'Yessss. Now try the soup.'

It was a very large bowl of soup. Bits of goo like gross green leaves floated in a liquid that was more yellow than egg yolk.

'Taste it!' said Nishi.

'Now?', asked Mum.

'Yes!'

Mum raised the spoon slowly to her mouth, and then quickly gulped it down.

'Mmmm... wow... you made it all by yourself?'

'Mmhmm,' said Nishi giggling. 'How do you like it? It was my own recipe.'

'I see.'

The next spoon went it in even more slowly.

'Mmm... That's delicious. I'm feeling better already.'

Nishi beamed with pride.

'Thank you so much, my dear,' said Mum. 'Could you get me a glass of water?'

'Ok,' said Nishi and bounced away to the kitchen.

When she came back, the bowl of soup was empty and Mum was fast asleep.

'That soup went quickly... she must've been really sick,' thought Nishi before closing the door behind her.

***

By the next morning, Mum was feeling well enough to move about the house. Nishi had left the kitchen spotlessly clean, so Mum wouldn't have a heart-attack and fall sick again. So when she came down to see the kitchen, it was yet another surprise.

Nishi was relieved that she would now see less of Laji Auntie, but something else had put her in an awful mood. Sitting on the lawn, she was angrily uprooting blades of grass, when Mum waived out to her from the living-room window. Nishi rushed in and hugged her tight.

'What's the matter?' asked Mum.

'Why does everyone have to fall sick all the time?' said Nishi frowning.

'Who else has fallen sick, sweetheart?'

'It's Subbu', said Nishi with a tear in her eye.

That morning, Nishi had found Subbu lying on his side, breathing heavily but barely moving. Worried, she had asked the building watchman if he knew why, and he had told her that Subbu had been eating from a plastic bag that had some stinky yellow stuff in it. Curiously, it had been lying on the ground outside her mum's bedroom window.

'Would you know anything about that, Mum?'

'Oh dear,' said Mum, clearing her throat, 'We better call the Vet.'

'Something tells me it was Laji aunty. She planned this because she hates me and she hates Subbu,' said Nishi, glaring at the first floor window.

'Now, now,' said Mum, 'We shouldn't go around blaming people unless we're absolutely sure.'

Nishi hung her head low as tears spilled from her eyes.

'Did you know that it was Subbu who put the idea into my head to

make you soup?'
said Nishi.
'Let me see...
what can we do
to make
him better?'
Nishi was so sad
she could
barely think.
'Do you think
if we did
some Kazukai
concentration,
we could come
up with an idea?'
Mum offered.

'Fine,' said Nishi. Anything was better than moping.

Soon, both Nishi and Mum were sitting opposite each other with
their eyes tightly shut.

Bzzzzz.

'Are the ideas coming, Mum?'

'Shhhhhh! Concentrate!'

Bzzzzzzzz.

Mum squeezed Nishi's palms and as they concentrated, the
buzzing in their heads got longer and longer, until—

Bzzzzzzzzzzzzzzzzzzzzzzzzzzzzzzzzzzzzzzzzzzz.

'SOUP!' cried Mum suddenly.

Nishi opened an eye. 'Soup? Are you sure about this, Mum?'

'Yes, of course! A visit from the Vet and some good homemade
broth ought to do him right. And maybe, from now on, we could
give him food everyday, so he doesn't have to eat from under
people's windows!' said Mum.

Now *that* was a great idea.

'Go get the Vet on the phone for me and I'll get things ready in the kitchen,' said Mum getting to her feet.

While they waited for the Vet to arrive, Nishi and Mum got busy preparing the special soup for Subbu.

On a piece of paper, Mum wrote down the ingredients:

2 cup of milk
1 cup of water
1 tea spoon of sugar
2 table spoons of all-purpose flour
1 table spoon of butter
1 chopped onion
1 chopped carrot
5 chopped leaves of spinach
5 mint leaves
A teaspoon of turmeric powder
A pinch of salt
A pinch of pepper

Gathering all the ingredients on the counter, Mum rolled up her sleeves and put the stove on a medium flame. On the stove she put a pot.

'Never do this on your own again unless there is a grown-up to watch you,' warned Mum.

'I promise I won't,' said Nishi.

Adding butter to the pot, Mum waited till it melted completely, and then carefully added the all-purpose flour.

'Why is it called all-purpose flour, Mum?'

'That's because you can use it to make all sorts of things like cake, cookies, pies, bread and whatever else you want, including soup!'

'Mmm... just the thought of it makes me hungry,' said Nishi dreamily, as she rubbed her stomach.

With a Whisk (that looked like a wiry bulb) Mum quickly whipped the two together, added the onion and slowly poured in milk.

After a few minutes, Nishi noticed that the liquid in the pot was thicker and bubblier. She smiled as she took in the aroma. This was way better than her own recipe.

To this, Mum added water, carrots and the chopped spinach leaves.

'Hey! I used those too!' Nishi exclaimed pointing at the bunch.

'Yes, I remember,' said Mum, raising an eyebrow.

To the broth, Mum added sugar, salt, pepper and turmeric powder and boiled it a bit longer before turning off the stove.

'We're almost done with our Soup,' said Mum, dusting her hands, 'But it's not complete until it has a name. Can you think of something?'

'Hmm....,' said Nishi, thoughtfully, as she put a spoonful in her mouth. A warm, comforting feeling took her over.

'Subbu Soup! How about we call it Subbu Soup?'

'Subbu Soup? That's a great name,' said Mum with a wink and a smile.

THE END

THE SNATCH

Story & Script
Anupam Arunachalam

Pencils and Inks
Ramanamanohar

Colours
Akshay Khadilkar

Letters
Pranay Bendre

OKAY, LET'S DO THIS. I'M THE **MARK**—THE VICTIM YOU'RE GOING TO STEAL FROM.

SMRITI WILL PLAY THE **STALL**. HER JOB IS TO DISTRACT THE MARK.

AND MALLIKA IS THE **DIP**. ONCE THE MARK IS DISTRACTED, SHE LIFTS THE WALLET.

FIRST, YOU'LL HAVE TO IDENTIFY WHERE THE PRIZE IS.

AS I TOLD YOU, THE BACK POCKET IS THE LEAST SAFE LOCATION. I WOULDN'T KEEP MY WALLET IN THERE.

THE STALL SHOULD NEVER WALK DIRECTLY TOWARDS THE MARK, NOR LOOK HIM IN THE EYE...

...THE BUMP SHOULD SEEM LIKE AN ACCIDENT...

WHOOPS!

...IT'S NOT NORMAL BEHAVIOUR TO SUDDENLY STOP WITHOUT LOOKING AROUND, SO THE STALL'S BEHAVIOUR MIGHT SEEM A LITTLE STRANGE ANYWAY...

132

A WEEK LATER—

BAAL BHARAT PUBLIC SCHOOL

HELP HELP

HELP! THIEF! THERE'S A THIEF IN THE BUILDING!

WHAT DO YOU MEAN, RANJIT SIR? IS SOMETHING MISSING?

SMRITI, WHAT'S GOING ON HERE?

I DON'T KNOW... I THINK RANJIT SIR HAS LOST SOMETHING.

THE TEST PAPER! IT WAS RIGHT THERE ON MY DESK! I'M SURE SOMEONE'S STOLEN IT!

I'D JUST GOT THE UNIT TEST PRINTED OUT. SOMEONE MUST HAVE SEEN ME PROOFREADING IT AS I WAS WALKING TO THE ROOM.

I LEFT IT HERE AND WENT OUT FOR A—

HUH? UH OH.

UMM... I'M SORRY, PEOPLE. FALSE ALARM. I GUESS IT'S HERE AFTER ALL. I MUSTN'T HAVE NOTICED...

GOOD OLD RANJIT SIR. SPOOKED AT THE SLIGHTEST.

MAN, THESE TEACHERS HAVE TO LEARN TO CHILL OUT.

SMRITI!

LOOK! THERE'S A FINGERPRINT ON THE TESTPAPER

WHA—?

AND IT LOOKS TOO SMALL TO BE RANJIT SIR'S.

IF SOMEONE STOLE THE PAPER AND RETURNED IT WHILE RANJIT SIR WAS JUST OUTSIDE THE ROOM, HE MUST STILL BE IN—

MALLI!

BEHIND THE CURTAINS.

HE'S STILL HERE!

MAYBE HE'S JUST GLAD HE GOT OUT OF THIS SAFE.

I DON'T THINK SO. THAT WASN'T RELIEF. HE'S SEEN THE PAPER.

BUT HOW? THERE JUST WASN'T ENOUGH TIME...

HE MUST HAVE A PHONE! HE TOOK A PICTURE OF IT!

OF COURSE! HE'S BEEN SHOWING OFF HIS NEW SMARTPHONE FOR A MONTH.

THAT CREEP! I CAN'T BELIEVE HE'S GOING TO GET AWAY WITH IT!

HEY, MALLI.

I THINK WE SHOULD LIBERATE MR SHAH OF THAT PHONE FOR A BIT.

HUH?

LET'S GET HIM!

YOU'RE ON, SIS!

139

140

GAME time with SEAN.

A day before I was scheduled to submit this month's feature, I had all my research in place to write a fairly in depth article about cycling and the Tour De France. I was happy with the research and was looking forward to stringing it all together... that was, until news of Sir Alex Ferguson's retirement broke.

Sir Alex Ferguson (SAF) manages Manchester United F.C. (Football Club), a team that participates in the English Premier League (EPL). In fact, a few weeks ago, Manchester United won the EPL title for the 2012-2013 season. This was the club's 20th EPL title. After securing this title, SAF announced he would be stepping down as guardian, caretaker and manager of the club.

This news is what led me to change this month's feature. I will cover cycling and the Tour De France next month, so all you cycling enthusiasts, do not be disheartened. However, for this month, in tribute to SAF, I'm going to take you through a list of the greatest football managers of all time.

Please note: This list of managers isn't in any particular order and is merely a collection of the best managers, in my opinion.

Sir Alex Ferguson

Before I get too carried away by my emotions, let me list just what SAF has won during his time as manager of Manchester United. During his 26 years at the club he's won a total of 13 EPL titles, ten Community Shields, five FA Cups, four League Cups and two European Cups. However SAF is regarded as the greatest manager of all time not just for the trophies he's won but also for the structure and backbone he gave the club. The club's state of the art training facility was his brainchild. The team's youth system, which delivered some of Manchester United and England's best players, was his idea. The football world

A statue of Sir Alex Ferguson installed in 2012

may never see another manager of his caliber again... but for the sake of the sport I sincerely hope they do.

Bob Paisley

Liverpool F.C. was blessed with two of the greatest football managers of all time. One was Bill Shankly and the other Bob Paisley. In fact, if it wasn't for SAF, Bob Paisley would be regarded as the most successful manager in English football history. In nine years as manager (1974-1983), he took Liverpool to six League Titles, three European Cups, one UEFA Cup, three League Cups, five Community Shields and a UEFA Super Cup. Paisley is the only manager to win three European Cups.

Vittorio Pozzo

Vittorio Pozzo was a tough manager, but his managerial style brought about results for Italy, especially during the first World Cup competitions. Pozzo lead Italy to two successive World Cups (1934 and 1938), a feat that has not been matched till date. In this time he also oversaw an unbeaten streak that lasted almost five years.

A few more along the way

This list isn't complete and it won't be. There are too many names left out for it to start to look full. So I'm just going to start listing the names of a few managers that I admire and hopefully you will go out and read about them further.

Jose Mourinho: Jose Mourinho hasn't only won everything, he's won it everywhere. He's won seven titles in four different countries including England and Spain.

Ottmar Hitzfeld: Omar Hitzfeld won 18 major titles in under 30 years as a manager. He is widely recognized as the greatest manager of the Bundesliga has ever seen.

Arsene Wenger: The only manager to lead an EPL team (Arsenal) through an entire season without losing a single game.

Pep Guardiola: In four seasons at Barcelona, Pep won a total of 13 trophies including three La Liga championships, two Champions League titles and also revolutionized the way the game is played.

Round Up

A football team is made up of good footballing talent. Whether it's for country or club, a team that consists of good football players will always stand a chance. However what makes these players a team is its management and in many cases its manager. The manager picks the team, balancing it out so that the best eleven players are on the field when the whistle is blown.

When a team fails, a manager shields his players and absorbs all the blame. When a team is victorious a manager quickly shifts into the shadows and lets the players collect all the accolades. A manager isn't someone that chases the limelight… he's the one that makes sure his team performs when the spotlight is shone on them.

Stay In Touch

As always if you have any feedback about this feature, and any aspect of a sport you feel needs more detailing do let me know. Also if there is any sport you'd like me to cover, drop me an email at **sean.dmello@ack-media.com** and I promise to read and reply to every one of your suggestions. Till next time then, keep playing and keep watching.

TaNTRi The MaNTRi
The Haunted Palace

Based on a story sent by
Anjana Murthy
Script: Rajani Thindiath
Illustrator: Prachi Killekar
Colourist: Umesh Sarode

LIFE'S BORING... EVERYTHING'S JUST THE SAME...

YOU KNOW, TANTRI. WE NEED SOME THRILL IN OUR LIVES TO KEEP IT INTERESTING.

AND **THAT'S** MY CUE!

EXACTLY, SIRE! THAT IS WHY I'VE PLANNED A SPECIAL HAUNTED CASTLE TOUR FOR YOU!

HAUNTED CASTLE TOUR ?!

YES! IT'S THE LATEST SENSATION!

PEOPLE PAY BIG BUCKS FOR THE EXPERIENCE!

BUT WE CAN EXPERIENCE IT FOR FREE – IN THE BLUE ROOM AT YOUR CASTLE IN CHANDRAGIRI! GHOSTS, BANSHEES, WEREWOLVES... THERE'VE BEEN ALL KINDS OF SIGHTINGS THERE!

ER... SHOULDN'T WE START WITH SOMETHING SMALL...?

SMALL ?! ROYALS SHOULD THINK **BIG** ! I'VE EVEN GOT A SPECIAL GHOSTBUSTER KIT FOR US !

YOU ARE RIGHT, TANTRI !

WE'LL TACKLE THE GHOSTS AND SEND THEM PACKING ! I'M SURE IT WOULD BE A UNIQUE EXPERIENCE !

I ASSURE YOU, SIRE, IT WOULD BE THE EXPERIENCE OF A LIFETIME !

AND SO THE ROYAL ENTOURAGE MADE ITS WAY TO CHANDRAGIRI –

I'LL LEAVE YOU TO REST, SIRE, WHILE I MAKE SPECIAL ARRANGEMENTS FOR TONIGHT !

I'LL TAKE A LOOK AROUND. IT'S BEEN AGES SINCE I'VE BEEN HERE.

I USED TO LOVE TO WATCH THE CROCODILES IN THE MOAT ! I WONDER HOW THEY'RE DOING ?

WHY NOT GO DOWN AND TAKE A LOOK ?

AS USUAL, TANTRI HAD A WICKED PLAN IN MIND, AND AS SOON AS HOOJA WAS OUT OF SIGHT –

ALOO RAM, ULLOO RAM, THE KING EXPECTS A THRILLING ADVENTURE AND WE MUST DO OUR BEST...

144

...AT HASTENING HIS END!

ALOO RAM, YOU'LL BE THE GHOST AND SCARE THE KING OUT TO THE TERRACE.

I'LL BE THE BEST GHOST YOU'VE EVER SEEN...ER... **NOT** SEEN!

AND ULLOO RAM, YOU'LL BE WAITING FOR THE KING ON THE TERRACE!

WAIT FOR THE KING TO REACH THE TERRACE WALL...

...AND THEN HOWL LIKE A WOLF...!

YOU CAN DEPEND ON ME, SIR!

THAT NIGHT –

SIRE, THE HOUR APPROACHES MIDNIGHT...

...TIME FOR GHOSTBUSTING, EH? SO, LET'S GET TO IT!

I FORGOT THE GHOSTBUSTING KIT! YOU LOOK AROUND, SIRE. I'LL BE WITH YOU IN FIVE MINUTES.

DON'T BE LONG...

...OR I'LL HAVE SENT THE GHOSTS PACKING AND YOU'LL MISS ALL THE ACTION!

FAMOUS LAST WORDS!! HEE HEE!

145

WHEN HOOJA REACHED THE BLUE ROOM –

HOOOOOWWL!

AAAAH !

WHERE DID THAT SOUND COME FROM ? AND...AND...WHO MADE IT !!

HOOOOWL!

EEUUW

NEVER THOUGHT GHOSTS COULD BE SO SCARY !!

HSSSHHAAH!

WHHSSHHH!

WHAT'S THAT ! THERE'S SOMETHING EVIL IN HERE !

146

147

HE HAS FALLEN OVER !! IT WAS EASIER THAN I THOUGHT !!

OUR DEAR KING HAS FALLEN OVER INTO THE MOAT ! THE CROCS WILL DEVOUR HIM !

WHAT A SAD DAY FOR ALL OF US... BOOHOOHOO !

WHAT'S THE MATTER, TANTRI ?

HOOJA HAS BEEN DEVOURED BY...**HOOJA** !

149

ODES TO SUPPANDI

CONTRIBUTOR: ANIK ROY
ARTIST: ARCHANA AMBERKAR
COLOURIST: PRANAY BENDRE

We went out fishing in my boat one day,
With my fishing net and the sun shining
bright in the bay,

We were deep into the sea
When I spotted a shoal of fish with glee!

I quickly told Suppandi
"Throw in the net, my friend"
As I was minding the oar at the other end,
"Splash!" came a sound of the net in the sea
And Suppandi was looking gladly, back at me.

After some time I told him to pull up the net,
For I was sure we had struck gold,
Suppandi replied "But sir, you told me to throw
out the net,
And I did exactly as I was told!"

One cold morning, I told Suppandi
to milk the cows in the shed,
He came back after some time
looking dejected instead,

"Sir," said he, "It's freezing cold out
there and I thought it would now
not be fair, to milk a cow even in my
dream, for I am sure we wouldn't get
milk but chilled ice-cream!"

150

Natasha's Big ADVENTURES

Hello Adventurers,

While growing up there was one book that always fascinated me. A book called *Alice's Adventures in Wonderland* by Lewis Carroll. I was completely enthralled by the novel, but one incident from the book always stood out for me. It was the moment when Alice follows the rabbit through the hole in the tree and emerges into a magical and mystical world at the other end.

My love for travelling and adventure meant that growing up, I would always look for a chance to disappear into a magical world that would appear out of nowhere. A few years down the line, during a caving trip to the Abbey Caves, in the North Island of New Zeland, my chance to disappear to a magical world finally came true.

Caving or as it's popularly called spelunking, is a lot of fun and it gives you the chance to explore caves and see things you never knew existed. People who go spelunking, do it for the thrill of adventure and don't go about exploring the caves in the name of research or study. My visit to the Abbey caves was my first experience with spelunking and as with everything I do, I was both excited and nervous.

As we started walking into the caves, the water level started rising and was soon all the way up to my waist. Although there was a bright afternoon sun outside, the moment you walked a few meters into the cave it was pitch dark... and that's where my Alice in Wonderland experience began. Like Alice, this unknown dark place spooked me at first.

However, as I trudged along I let the rest of my senses take over, since my eyes were rendered temporarily useless. I could hear the bats above my head and the continuous trickling of water in the distance. My skin could feel a cold draft. I used my hands and feet to trace my path so I wouldn't get into a jam.

Looking back, I'm glad my eyes were rested, because as soon as I got inside the cave, I was witness to one of the most beautiful sights I've ever seen. The first mystical sight that catches your eyes is the wonderfully mysterious light of the glowworms. Glowworms are little insects that hang from the ceilings of the caves. They have a spark on their bottom, but when you look at them in a dark cave, they look like stars shinning in the night sky. But it's not just glowworms that you see inside. There is beautiful stalagmite and stalactite, and creatures that live below the surface—creatures you'd never get to see otherwise.

Inside the Abbey Caves, I finally knew how Alice felt when she entered Wonderland. That sudden change from the normal world to this mystical land of allure and aura, is a feeling I'll never forget.

However, you don't need to travel to New Zealand to go caving. Meghalaya in India has loads of caves that are open to enthusiastic cavers. In fact, some of the deepest and longest of the caves in South Asia are located in the Khasi Hills in Meghalaya.

My experience of spelunking made me fall in love with nature all over again. How could it not? Nature and adventure allowed me to have my very own magical journey. What about you? Wouldn't you love to see the world that exists behind that dark passage? Trust me, it's breathtaking.

Natasha Sahgal is a writer for National Geographic Traveller India.
You can read more of her stories on natgeotraveller.in

Get in touch! Email: **natasha.sahgal@ack-media.com** Post: Natasha Sahgal, ACK Media, 3rd Floor, Krishna House, Raghuvanshi Mills Compound, Lower Parel, Mumbai 400013.

THE MALABAR CIVET FILES

Ecologists go in hot pursuit of one of the rarest and most endangered animals in the Western Ghats

by **Siddharth Rao**

As I turned on the spotlight to check the trail in front of me, a pair of large orange eyes shone from the tree ahead. I forgot about the leeches that were clinging to my leg, and focused the light on the tree from which the 'eyeshine' appeared – a brown palm civet sat there watching me. A nocturnal carnivore, this civet inhabits the forests of the Western Ghats, and is one of four species of civets found in peninsular India. The other ones found here are the common palm civet, the small Indian civet and the Malabar civet.

This encounter happened when I was walking a transect deep in the rainforests of Kerala as part of my research to establish the presence of the Malabar civet in the wild. One of India's rarest mammals, the Malabar civet was thought to be extinct, until a fresh skin was recovered from a hunter in Kerala in 1991. The Malabar civet is currently listed as 'Critically Endangered', and its population trend is officially unknown. Few biologists have studied this animal and little is known about its ecology and distribution.

The first long-term study on the Malabar civet was initiated in 2006 by the Wildlife Trust of India, a conservation organisation I was working at at the time. My colleagues from the Wildlife Trust of India and I, surveyed thousands of kilometres of forests along the Western Ghats of Karnataka and Kerala in search of this elusive mammal. We walked transects and conducted interviews with local forest-dwelling communities. We

Sniffing Out the

Morphology: The Malabar civet (*Viverra civettina*) is approximately four feet long from nose to tail and is estimated to weigh up to 8kg. The tail has five to six black and white bands and the fur on its coat has patches of white and black hair. The neck has two distinctive large black stripes, while there is a prominent crest of dark hair along its back.

Ecology: The Malabar civet is thought to eat a variety of small prey and is probably

154

Artwork: Somesh Kumar

set up camera traps to record possible civet movement in remote forests. After two years of searching, we still did not find concrete evidence of the Malabar civet. However, we got pretty close many times, with local hunters reporting captures. To prove the continued existence of the species, though, we would still need a skin sample, a live animal or a photograph.

The last live Malabar civet was recorded in the early 1930s, after which only hunted specimens have shown up sporadically as

evidence of the existence of the species. Although there is no photographic proof of the Malabar civet, scientists use information obtained from museum specimens as reference. But the lack of evidence from the field has not stopped the investigation into the ecology of the Malabar civet. Luckily, researchers are able to use technology to find out more about such rare animals. A study on the phylogenetics (evolutionary relatedness) of this civet is currently underway, where small-carnivore researchers are examining DNA of the Malabar civet in order to trace its ancestry.

Musky Mammal

nocturnal like most other civets. A major reason for its decline is loss of habitat as forests in the region have been turned into rubber plantations.

Conservation: Some researchers believe that the Malabar civet is an introduced species that was brought to south India for the purpose of musk trade (used in traditional medicine) and a few animals escaped into the wild.

In the meantime, field-based surveys continue in the hope of finding a Malabar civet in the wild. Long-term field surveys combined with lab-based investigations are essential when looking for rare species. And who knows, someday there might be a breakthrough. The next time you are in the forests of the Western Ghats, keep your eyes open and cameras ready. Remember that if you take a photo of the Malabar civet, you will be the first to do so. Happy clicking! ●

Siddharth Rao is a conservation biologist, wildlife photographer and Director of ARRS.

156

THE HAPPY COBBLER

Script: L. Prabhu
Illustrator: Savio Mascarenhas
Colourist: Umesh Sarode

KING VIKTOR OF LAVORIA WOULD DISGUISE HIMSELF AND MINGLE WITH HIS PEOPLE TO FIND OUT HOW THEY WERE FARING UNDER HIS RULE.

LATE, ONE EVENING, AS HE WAS WALKING THROUGH THE POOREST PART OF HIS CAPITAL CITY –

DUM-DEE-DUM-DEE-DUM ! LIFE'S SO HARD BUT IT COULD BE WORSE. DUM-DEE-DUM- DEE-DUM !

UNBELIEVABLE !

THIS PLACE IS NOT FIT FOR DOGS YET SOMEBODY HERE IS SO HAPPY HE'S SINGING !

DUM-DEE-DUM-DEE -DUM !

KNOCK! KNOCK!!

WHO'S THERE ?

A TRAVELLER WHO WANTS TO TALK.

COME IN !

WELCOME TO MY HUMBLE ABODE !

HUMBLE IS TOO GOOD A WORD FOR THIS PIG STY !

I'VE HEARD THE KING HAS INTRODUCED A LICENCE FOR COBBLERS. DID YOU GET ONE?

NO, I DIDN'T HAVE THREE COPPERS! THE KING MUST BE POOR INDEED TO TAKE FROM COBBLERS!

AH, YES...AHEM...

SO YOU DIDN'T DO ANY COBBLING TODAY... DIDN'T THAT WORRY YOU?

NOT A BIT.

I CAME ACROSS SOME MEN WHO WERE ON THEIR WAY TO THE ROYAL FOREST TO COLLECT WOOD TO SELL, AND I JOINED THEM. I COLLECTED SOME WOOD TOO.

AND SOLD IT. I GOT ABOUT AS MUCH AS I MAKE THROUGH COBBLING. AS I SAID, GOD PROVIDES!

HE DOES, DOES HE?

THE NEXT DAY WHEN THE COBBLER AND OTHERS WERE GOING TOWARDS THE WOODS –

HALT!

NO GATHERING WOOD FROM THE ROYAL FORESTS FROM NOW ON!

HEY, THAT'S NOT FAIR!

TELL THE KING! HE MAKES THE RULES!!

ANYONE CAUGHT SNEAKING INTO THE FOREST WILL BE SEVERELY PUNISHED!!

LATE THAT EVENING WHEN THE KING ARRIVED AT THE COBBLER'S HOUSE —

NO SONG! I'VE SILENCED HIM AT LAST!!

PERHAPS GONE TO BED HUNGRY AND...!!!

DUM-DEE-DUM-DEE DUM!

HOW CAN YOU AFFORD TO SING, YOU FOOL?!!!

WHAT?

I...I MEAN HOW'S THAT YOU'RE STILL SO CAREFREE? I'VE HEARD THAT THE KING HAS BANNED PEOPLE FROM COLLECTING WOOD IN THE ROYAL FORESTS!!

163

DID YOU EARN ENOUGH TO EAT?

CERTAINLY! DO I LOOK LIKE I'M STARVING?

WHEN MY FRIENDS AND I WERE TOLD WE COULD NOT COLLECT WOOD, WE DISPERSED. AND THEN SOMEBODY TOLD ME THAT THE PALACE GUARDS WERE SHORT OF SOLDIERS. I WENT THERE AND ENLISTED!

SO YOU'RE A SOLDIER NOW!

ONLY TILL I SAVE ENOUGH TO GET A COBBLER'S LICENCE. FORTUNATELY THEY PAY DAILY WAGES SO I COULD EAT. AS I SAID, THE LORD PROVIDES!!

NOT FOR LONG, NOT FOR LONG, MY FRIEND!

THE NEXT DAY THE COBBLER WAS GIVEN HIS UNIFORM WHICH INCLUDED A HELMET AND A SWORD. THE COBBLER STRAPPED ON THE SWORD...

...AND WENT TO THE PARADE GROUNDS. THERE –

I HAVE AN ANNOUNCEMENT TO MAKE... THE KING HAS DECREED THAT FROM NOW ON THERE WILL BE NO DAILY WAGES!

EVERYBODY WILL BE PAID AT THE END OF THE MONTH, INCLUDING THE NEW RECRUITS!

164

IN THE EVENING WHEN THE KING TRIUMPHANTLY MADE HIS WAY TO THE COBBLER'S HOUSE –

NOT A SOUND! MUST BE WORRIED SICK ABOUT HOW TO PULL ON TILL THE END OF THE MONTH. NOW HE KNOWS WHOM HE HAS TO THANK FOR THE CAREFREE LIFE HE HAS BEEN ENJOYING SO FAR!

LET'S SEE WHAT HE HAS TO SAY!

KNOCK! KNOCK!!

(CRONCH)... (CRUNCH)... YOU! WELCOME!! PLEASE COME IN!

YOU'RE EATING! I-I MEAN I THOUGHT YOU WERE NOT SINGING BECAUSE...OH, NEVER MIND!

I WAS WORRIED ABOUT YOU. I HEARD THAT THE PALACE GUARD HAS STOPPED GIVING DAILY WAGES. HOW ARE YOU MANAGING?

THE LORD PROVIDES!

I PAWNED MY SWORD.

PAWNED YOUR SWORD! BUT WON'T YOU BE FOUND OUT TOMORROW?

I PAWNED ONLY THE BLADE. IT CAN BE DETACHED FROM THE HILT, AND IT IS MADE OF THE FINEST STEEL!

AS LONG AS THE CAPTAIN CAN SEE THE HILT IN MY SCABBARD HE WON'T KNOW THE SWORD IS MISSING!

AND IT'S ONLY FOR A FEW DAYS TILL I GET MY PAY. THEN I'LL REDEEM THE SWORD.

FOR ALL HIS SIMPLICITY, HE'S QUITE RESOURCEFUL!

WILL YOU HAVE SOME CHEESE? I MANAGED TO GET A STALK OF CELERY TOO...

NO, NO...I'VE GOT TO GO... GOODNIGHT!

DUM-DEE-DUM-DEE-DUM!

ONCE AGAIN HE HAS OUTWITTED ME! WELL, SOON HIS SONG WILL DRY UP IN HIS THROAT!!

THE NEXT MORNING WHEN THE PALACE GUARDS WERE BEING BRIEFED ABOUT THEIR DUTIES FOR THE DAY –

THE KING!

WHY IS THE KING COMING? I...I HOPE THEY'VE NOT DISCOVERED THAT I'M AN ESCAPED CONVICT!

167

168

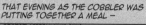
THAT EVENING AS THE COBBLER WAS PUTTING TOGETHER A MEAL —

DUM...DEE... DUM...DEE....

WHO'S THAT!

KNOCK KNOCK!!

??!!!!

YOUR MAJESTY!

WITHOUT MY DISGUISE, THIS TIME!

I'VE COME TO TAKE YOU TO MY PALACE! I WANT TO MAKE YOU A MINISTER IN MY GOVERNMENT!

ME? A MINISTER! THAT'S A BIG JUMP FOR ME, YOUR MAJESTY! BUT AS I ALWAYS SAY...

THE LORD PROVIDES!

The Fab Five

Based on a story sent by **Ramendra Kumar**
Script: Rajani Thindiath
Illustrator & Colourist: Durgesh Velhal

SCHOOL HAD RE-OPENED AND THE FUNDU FOUR – VICKY, PETER, RAJ AND MIRZA, WERE MEETING AFTER A LONG TIME –

I CAN'T BELIEVE THIS! MIRZA'S HERE BEFORE US!

HEY MIRZA, DOESN'T LOOK LIKE YOU ENJOYED YOUR COUSIN'S VISIT!

DON'T TALK ABOUT THAT BORE! VACATION DRAGGED ON AND ON.

BUT I'VE NEWS FOR YOU. WHICH DO YOU WANT FIRST – BAD NEWS OR GOOD NEWS?

THE GOOD NEWS! I DON'T WANT TO BEGIN THE SCHOOL YEAR ON A BAD NOTE!

OKAY, THE GOOD NEWS IS YOU, PETER AND I ARE IN THE SAME DIVISION – A!

170

COOL!

WHAT ABOUT VICKY?

THAT'S THE BAD NEWS – VICKY'S IN DIVISION B...WITH HYDER!

HYDER, THE BULLY! I'M DONE FOR!

DON'T WORRY, VICKY! JUST TELL US IF HE TRIES TO ACT SMART WITH YOU!

AS FOR US, WE CAN ALWAYS CATCH UP DURING RECESS!

IF YOU SAY SO!

A WEEK LATER, DURING RECESS –

HEY, VICKY! WHY THE LONG FACE?

YOU LOOK AS IF YOU HAVE HAD YOUR ALGEBRA HOMEWORK FOR BREAKFAST!

THAT PEST HYDER! HE MADE ME THE LAUGHING STOCK OF THE CLASS!

WHY, WHAT DID HE DO?

WE HAD A FREE PERIOD – THE ART TEACHER WAS ABSENT TODAY. SO I WENT TO THE LIBRARY TO RETURN A BOOK...

...WHEN I RETURNED I WAS GREETED WITH HOWLS OF LAUGHTER! HYDER HAD DRAWN A PIG ON THE BOARD AND HE LOOKED LIKE ME, SPECS AND ALL!

ONE PUNCH SHOULD TAKE CARE OF HIM!

NO, MIRZA – HE'LL RAT ON US TO THE PRINCI AND THAT'LL BECOME A MAJOR ISSUE! LET ME THINK OF SOMETHING.

I'VE GOT IT! THIS IS WHAT WE'LL DO...

...AND RAJ OUTLINED HIS PLAN.

THE NEXT DAY, DURING GAMES PERIOD, VICKY WAS PLAYING A GAME OF CHESS WITH HIS MATHS TEACHER, RAMESH IYENGAR –

SMART MOVE, VICKY! NOW WHAT IF I MOVE MY...

THAT BALDY IYENGAR CAN'T TEACH FOR NUTS!

DON'T LET HIM CATCH YOU SAY THAT, HYDER, OR YOU'VE HAD IT!

HAH! I'M NOT AFRAID OF THAT FATHEADED FOOL!

WE'LL CONTINUE THIS GAME TOMORROW, VICKY!

OKAY, SIR.

THERE'S NO ONE IN THE CORRIDOR!

RAJ, PETER, DID YOU SEE HYDER AROUND?

YES, I SAW HIM GOING TOWARDS THE BASKETBALL COURT. DO YOU WANT ME TO GET HIM?

YES, ASK HIM TO MEET ME IN THE STAFF ROOM, IMMEDIATELY!

YES, SIR.

HEY HYDER, IYENGAR SIR WANTS YOU IN THE STAFF ROOM.

WHAT FOR?

ASK HIM!

THIS SHOULD BE FUN!

SOMETIME LATER, HYDER CAME OUT OF THE STAFFROOM FUMING —

BALDY'S GONE MAD! HEARING THINGS!

HOW COULD I BE CALLING HIM NAMES FROM THE CORRIDOR WHEN I WAS AT THE BASKETBALL COURT!

MAY BE LIKE THIS, "THAT BALDY IYENGAR CAN'T TEACH FOR NUTS"!

HEY! THAT'S—THAT'S MY VOICE! YOU MIMICKED MY VOICE!

YOU ARE RIGHT, EINSTEIN! AND IF YOU DON'T WANT A REPEAT PERFORMANCE YOU BETTER STOP TROUBLING VICKY!

I'LL TELL IYENGAR SIR ABOUT THIS!

MY DEAR HYDER, YOU HAVE NO PROOF!

STAY AWAY FROM VICKY AND WE'LL STAY AWAY FROM YOU!

I'LL GET YOU ALL FOR THIS!

A MONTH PASSED AFTER THIS INCIDENT. ONE DAY, HYDER WAS CYCLING HOME AFTER TUITION –

ISN'T THAT RAJ ? AND THOSE BOYS...THEY'RE THE ROWDIES FROM ST. GEORGE COLLEGE !

HEY, WHAT'S GOING ON HERE ?

MR. SMARTY PANTS NEEDS A LESSON IN MANNERS.

HE NEEDS TO LEARN NOT TO POKE HIS NOSE WHERE IT'S NOT NEEDED.

YOU WERE HARASSING THAT POOR DOG AND I JUST TOLD YOU TO STOP !

SO, YOU THINK YOU ARE SOME SUPERMAN ?

NO, BUT I'M NOT A NINNY TO STAND FOR SOMETHING LIKE THAT EITHER !

WELL THEN, WE SHOULD REWARD YOU FOR YOUR GOOD DEED !

CUT IT OUT, GUYS ! TAKE ON SOMEONE YOUR OWN SIZE !

THEN YOU SHOULD DO !

HEY GUYS, LEAVE ME OUT OF THIS ! SEE, I'M LEAVING !

YOUR FRIEND HAS RUN AWAY !

UNFORTUNATELY YOU CAN'T DO THE SAME !

174

NOW WE'LL TEACH YOU A LESSON YOU'LL NEVER FORGET!

WILL YOU?

?!!

THANKS, HYDER. I THOUGHT YOU'D RUN AWAY BUT IT WAS DECENT OF YOU TO GET HELP.

I KNEW I COULDN'T FIGHT THOSE ROWDIES ON MY OWN, RAJ, SO I JUST WENT AND GOT YOUR FRIENDS.

THE FOUR FRIENDS HAD NO MORE PROBLEMS WITH HYDER AFTER THAT. IN FACT, HYDER BECAME SO FRIENDLY WITH THEM THAT THE GROUP SOON BECAME KNOWN AS THE FAB FIVE!

PENCIL HEAD

You will need:

Pencil, Sketch Pen and Ruler, Tinted Paper (Any colour)
A Pair of Scissors, Cutter and Glue

Instructions:

1. Take a sheet of tinted paper and cut out a rectangular piece (length = 8cm; breadth = 7cm).

2. Divide the length into two parts of 3cm and 5cm respectively. In the 5cm space, draw horizontal lines on the top and bottom, as shown.

3. To the left side of the space between these lines, draw a smiling face.

4. With a cutter, make slits along the lines drawn, for ears.

5. Cut the top portion (measuring 3cm) into thin strips.

6. Use the pencil to curl these strips, as shown.

7. Next, glue the pencil firmly to the back of the rectangle's right end such that the top of the pencil is in line with the top horizontal lines.

8. Slowly, wind the piece around the pencil; the face should come right in front and the ears will stand out as flaps.

Curl the strips with the pencil.

9. Your pencil head is ready. Make many such pencil heads with funny faces for all your pencils.

Craft idea: Prachi Killekar